SOUTH
CHINA
SEA

SULU
SEA

8

Kota Kinabalu

Sandakan

Bandar Seri
Begawan

SABAH

BRUNEI

Miri

9

CELEBES
SEA

BUNGURAN
ISLANDS

Tarakan

AYSIA

SARAWAK

Kuching

BORNEO

Pontianak

EQUATOR

KALIMANTAN

Balikpapan

Palu

MAKASSAR STRAIT

Palangkaraya

SULAWESI

BELITUNG

Banjarmasin

PULAU LAUT

INDONESIA

Ujung Pandan

JAVA
SEA

Semarang

MADURA

JAVA

Surabaya

Jogyakarta

BALI

LOMBOK

Mataram

Denpasar

SUMBAWA

Trevesia burckii Ghost's foot **Daun tapak rimau/Daun tapak hantu**

Tropical
RAIN FOREST
in South~East Asia
~ A PICTORIAL JOURNEY

Photography and Text by
Ken Rubeli

TROPICAL PRESS SDN. BHD.
29, JALAN RIONG
59100 KUALA LUMPUR
MALAYSIA

First published 1986
Reprinted 1987
Reprinted 1988

ISBN 967-73-0013-X

Design and layout by the author
TYPESETTING, COLOUR SEPARATION,
PRINTING, AND BINDING BY
ART PRINTING WORKS SDN. BHD.
29 JALAN RIONG, 59100 KUALA LUMPUR,
MALAYSIA

For the forest itself...
and for all those
concerned for its future.

CONTENTS

GSN

PREFACE

The image and reality

This book is coloured ink fixed to a page. It is a collection of flat rectangles. A photograph can rarely evoke more than a suggestion of its subject in reality, and this is especially so when the subject is as rich in non-visual attributes as is the tropical rain forest. Nevertheless it is hoped that the evocations of these pages will stimulate in readers a desire to explore for themselves living examples of this forest and its rich variety of plant and animal life.

In the course of a few days in the rain forest, a visitor can expect to encounter only a tiny fraction of what a resident photographer can capture on film over several years; yet these pictures displayed represent only a miniscule part of what the forest as a whole contains. This pictorial journey can offer only a superficial understanding of such a diverse and complex natural environment. There should, however, be no important aspect of the South-East Asian tropical rain forest that has not at least been touched upon.

Ultimately this book is a plea for the conservation of the rain forest. It aims to encourage the development of a personal relationship with nature, and the establishment in some measure of a spiritual dependence upon the existence of unspoiled wilderness. Thus may be nurtured a profound respect for nature. Such respect gives birth to a conviction, not just that tropical rain forest ought to be conserved, but that it *must* be conserved.

*   *   *   *   *   *   *   *

What is tropical rain forest?

The tropical rain forest of South East Asia as represented in this book is the forest found on the large islands of Sumatra and Borneo, on the westernmost tip of Java, and down the Malay Peninsula from southern Thailand to Singapore. It does not, however, include the forest of mangrove flats, heathlands (kerangas), peat swamp, or fresh-water swamp, nor that of sandy coastal plains—although technically all these can fall within the definition of tropical rain forest, and all these do occur in tropical South-East Asia. This book explores the tall forest prevailing in non-swampy lowland areas both flat and undulating, and the different kinds of vegetation and wildlife encountered as one ascends into the mountains, or chances upon limestone. Most of the photographs were taken in Malaysia; many are from Peninsular Malaysia, and some from the Bornean states of Sabah and Sarawak. There are just a few pictures from Sumatra and southern Thailand.

Still, the scope of the work is by no means narrow. In its general character, the lowland rain forest shown here is very similar to lowland tropical rain forest in Central and West Africa, the Amazon Basin and Central America, New Guinea and coastal north-eastern Australia, and in other parts of Asia where pockets of rain forest occur: south-western India, Sri Lanka, Burma, southern China, and Taiwan. A similar sort of structure and atmosphere will be found in the forests of all of these places: an evergreen environment, dimly-lit, breezeless, intensely humid, with tall buttressed trees as well as a great variety of other vegetation forms, and a rich diversity of plant and animal species.

It is true that some rain-forest areas (those in southern Thailand for example) display a greater degree of seasonality than others. Where certain tree species lose all their leaves during the short dry season, such forests are technically set apart as semi-evergreen. The difference, however, is hardly apparent to the non-specialist, and despite rain-shadow effects giving rise to this semi-evergreen forest even in some southern parts of the Malay Peninsula, few local residents would recognise one part of the forest as being different from another.

100 million years old?

It is commonly stated that the tropical rain forest of South-East Asia is more than 100 million years old. This is rather misleading, but true in the sense that some nomadic tribes have a heritage going back thousands of years. Over this period people of the tribe might have moved the focus of their activity from one geographical region to another and perhaps back again; their customs might have changed with time, and even their physical characteristics might have altered. But genetically there has been a continuity throughout.

100 million years ago the rain forest had few if any flowering plants, and so its appearance was quite different from that of the forest today. Its geographical distribution, too, was probably different. But it evolved continuously throughout this period. It never completely disappeared, to be replaced by a different type of vegetation with a different genealogy.

The mountains of the Malay Peninsula have been geologically stable, without major uplift, or folding, or subsidence and new deposition, for an estimated 130 million years; they have supported plant life of some kind throughout this time. 30 million years ago all of what is now northern and eastern Borneo was under the sea. About 15 million years ago a process of geological upheavals began, resulting in the uplift and folding that formed the present Bornean mountain ranges (excluding Gunung Kinabalu, which was thrust up only during the past two million years). Borneo thus became a much larger island. Within the past 20 million years Sumatra, too, has undergone dramatic geological change.

Changes of a different kind have occurred in the last two million years, with the passage of the Ice Ages. As water became locked up in extending polar ice caps, sea levels fell; most of the South China Sea became dry land, and Sumatra, Java, and Borneo all became connected to each other and to the Malay Peninsula and Indo-China. At least four Ice Ages came and went, all brought about by major fluctuations in world climate. It appears that the tropical rain forest, formerly finding conditions suitable for growth as far north as Indo-China, was effectively driven from the higher latitudes during these periods of cooler, drier climate. It was largely replaced either by montane forest extending down to lower altitudes, or by deciduous forest or savanna (grassland with scattered trees) extending southwards across the lowlands. Only in areas close to the equator and in small remnant pockets of suitable climate elsewhere could tropical rain forest continue to survive. However, during these cool periods the land bridges provided avenues for the migration and intermingling of rain-forest plant and animal species throughout the equatorial zone of South-East Asia. The more extensive montane habitats also enabled mountain plants and animals to disperse widely through the tropics from northern and southern temperate regions.

As each Ice Age receded and the climate became warmer and wetter again, it seems that the tropical rain forest surviving in Sumatra, Borneo, and in parts of the Malay Peninsula might have served as a refuge and reservoir from which rain-forest species could then have progressively recolonised surrounding areas as the climate became more favourable.

Much of this is conjecture; but it does help to explain the presence, in the higher altitudes on Kinabalu, of isolated plant species whose closest relatives are found in the Himalayas and New Zealand. It also suggests that as recently as ten to fifteen thousand years ago (when there was still a glacial cap on Kinabalu) areas such as the lowlands of Taman Negara in Peninsular Malaysia, at about 4° latitude, might have carried a forest substantially different in species composition and overall character from that of the rain forest there today.

The diversity of species

In a few hectares of a conifer forest in Canada or a eucalypt forest in Australia, it is common to find only two or three species making up 90 per cent or more of the forest trees, and probably no more than 20 other kinds of plants present in the understorey. Standing on one spot in lowland tropical rain forest, within arm's reach there might easily be a dozen different kinds of plants, and within view ten times that number, including probably 30 to 40 different kinds of trees. From algae and mosses up to the flowering plants, and in animal life as well, there is an astonishing diversity of species. How does one account for this tropical extravaganza?

Three factors seem to apply. The first must be stated in negative terms. In the harsher climates of higher latitudes, plants and animals require special adaptations to survive in conditions which may be highly unfavourable for a major part of the year: a blanket of winter snow, for example, or a long period of summer drought. Any genetic variations on existing species face a slim chance of survival since they must be suitably equipped to endure both natural competition and the rigours of harsh seasons. But in an equatorial environment where the soil is constantly moist and there is abundant sunshine providing continuous warmth, there would seem to be significantly less reason for a genetic mutation *not* to survive. The tropical rain forest is a supremely benign environment for the development of new species.

This factor links with the second one: the immensely long period of continuous evolution. Within this period, cataclysmic events like the Ice Ages might have added further to the diversity of plant and animal species. Where rain forest survived only in scattered refuges, isolation of species and local adaptation allowed differentiation of forms. When re-united with their neighbours, some of these forms had become sufficiently differentiated in structure or behaviour to be unable to interbreed with what previously had been their own kin. Thus new species arose to take their place beside the old.

The third factor which tends to enhance species diversity is the complex structure of the rain forest. This provides a three-dimensional framework with niches for plants and animals of many different forms and life-patterns. The barbed extensions of the leaf shafts in most climbing palms enable them to climb only where there is a continuous ladder of vegetation all the way to the tree-tops; the rain-forest structure provides this. The multi-layered structure of the canopy necessitates that small light-loving plants grow not on the dim forest floor, but higher up; thus a great diversity of epiphytic plant species has evolved in the tropical rain forest.

Much remains to be learned about the process of evolution and the development of new species, and many old ideas are now being critically re-examined. The tropical rain forest in South-East Asia, with its unusual history, is a prime area for scientific study. Undoubtedly there are many plant and animal species yet to be discovered, and the ways plants and animals interact in the functioning of the forest are still little understood. Alas, as world-wide scientific interest increasingly focuses on the tropical rain forest, areas of undisturbed forest are rapidly dwindling.

The half-eaten cake

In Sumatra, Borneo, southern Thailand, and Peninsular Malaysia roughly half of the land area has been cleared of forest. Where forest still stands, large areas have already been exploited for timber. Most of the land that remains wholly undisturbed is covered by mountain forest since here the timber and the land generally have little commercial value. The lowland rain forest is the tallest, and also the richest in plant and animal species. This is the most severely threatened forest zone; for it is the lowland areas that offer a wealth of timber for harvesting, and offer terrain most suitable for agricultural development.

With careful planning, it would be possible to set aside lowland reserves for sustained-yield timber production under skilled forest management; sites confirmed as suitable for agriculture could, where necessary, be cleared and developed for the production of a variety of crops; key areas of mountain forest could be reserved as catchments; and selected areas of important scenic and scientific value could be protected permanently as core zones of large National Parks.

The reality fails to match this ideal situation, particularly with regard to National Parks. It is true that National Parks and Wildlife Reserves have been set up by concerned governments throughout South-East Asia. But wherever there are those in government committed to maintaining and augmenting these reserves, there are others who feel there are more pressing priorities. Areas previously designated as protected may be violated in the name of fast and high financial returns from logging, and for politically expedient land development schemes. Mining operations, highways, and hydro-electric dams also take their toll. In addition there are the problems within protected areas of timber-stealing and wildlife-poaching, as well as the delicate issue of forest clearing by tribal communities for shifting cultivation.

Priorities in rain-forest conservation

Conservation is a matter of priorities. The first priority must be satisfaction of the basic needs of the people. Without this, no degree of enforcement or education can hope to prevent the poaching of wildlife for food, nor the illegal cutting of timber for fuel. The second priority is justice in administration. The ready wealth that may be illicitly gained by authorities who approve issue of logging licences for protected rain-forest areas is a huge temptation to the corrupt, as, at a lesser scale, is the highly profitable trade in tiger skins, rhinoceros horn, and other anatomic parts of protected species, for trophies or for their imagined medicinal qualities.

The third priority, closely linked with the first, is firm long-term planning. Exploitation of the natural environment continues on a massive scale in many parts of South-East Asia with little or no apparent concern for future generations. Careless timber-felling causes excessive damage to remaining trees, and haphazard log extraction results in extensive soil disturbance, creating long-term erosion and stream-pollution problems. Reforestation of logged areas is the exception, not the rule. Much of the forest is left to rehabilitate itself, often severely depleted of desirable timber species for subsequent harvests. Foresters are well aware of the silvicultural principles to be applied for sustained-yield management, but too often the will is lacking to see principles put into practice.

Planning is critical in other areas too. Future water supplies are threatened by forest removal and soil disturbance on steep slopes in mountain regions. Too little value is placed on the importance of forest areas in maintaining climatic stability. Education towards limitation of population growth is an aspect of long-term planning of paramount importance to far more than just conservation of tropical rain forest; yet, outside Singapore, there is little sign in South-East Asia of concerted government effort in this vital field.

To assume that without major achievements in all these fields the existing National Parks and Wildlife Reserves of South-East Asia will survive with their boundaries and wildlife population intact, even as far as the year 2000, is a serious delusion. The timber industry in particular, with its powerful local and international lobbying forces, will exert massive pressure for relaxation of controls in nature reserves as timber supplies elsewhere are exhausted. For Parks and Reserves, financial returns from local and foreign tourism will always appear insignificant when matched against those from logging; but economists must accept that the returns from protected wilderness flow continuously year after year and cannot only be measured in direct financial terms.

The greatest challenge lies in the fulfilment of the first priority. In order to finance development projects that will contribute towards satisfaction of the basic needs of the human population, governments in South-East Asia today rely heavily on exploitation of natural resources. To South-East Asian ears, the cry from the west to "save the rain forests" rings hollow, coming as it does from countries which have very largely destroyed their own natural forests in order to establish the foundations of their industrial and agricultural economies. These wealthier countries will benefit if the rain forests do gain adequate protection. They must therefore be prepared to contribute, directly or indirectly, towards the cost. On the other hand, in order to attract such aid, those governments bearing direct responsibility for the rain forests must identify, and do everything possible to preserve for the present at least, large representative samples of virgin tropical rain forest.

National Parks and national development

Conservation is a positive step in national development. A National Park is not land set aside to be idle, but to serve many productive roles: As a living museum—providing foundation for national pride through preservation of natural heritage; as a factory complex—providing cool fresh oxygen-rich air, reliable rainfall, and clean dependable water supplies; as a recreation area—providing opportunities for human relaxation, both physical and mental, in healthy peaceful surroundings; as a place of adventure—providing an environment not wholly predictable, and a source of wonder and discovery to challenge and extend human capabilities; as a nature-study area—providing an undisturbed living resource for environmental education; as a storehouse—providing, for the future benefit of humankind, possible medicinal sources and stocks of plants and animals potentially valuable for food production; as a field laboratory—providing a pure natural ecosystem, rich in stimulus to scientific enquiry towards the understanding of natural phenomena; as a gene bank—providing organisms for biological control of diseases, and wild breeding-stock for improvement of forest-derived food species and horticultural plants; and, of most profound importance, as a shrine—providing communication with a world existing before humans appeared on Earth, and offering an insight into the true position of humanity, originating in, and wholly dependent upon, nature.

The long-term view

Humankind and nature *can* prosper side by side; a secure and balanced future demands nothing less than this state of harmony. For a small investment now, conservation of nature can bring, to both individual and nation, benefits whose value will grow with the passage of time. A great responsibility rests with those now in government to ensure that tracts of tropical rain forest are preserved pure and inviolable for the sake of all that lives within them, and for the sake of all humanity now and in the future. The alternative is that in a matter of decades a forest that has developed over millions of years will be reduced to remote and tattered relics, to words and memories, to specimens in museums, and to pictorial records on film and in books.

Sungai Tembeling, Pahang, Peninsular Malaysia (in flood)

T THE RIVER

IT is fitting that this journey should begin along the river. For the journey is one in homage to nature, and the waterways are a part of nature. Rivers are roads that make no human mark upon the landscape. Rather, they consolidate the natural scene, drawing all together into one: the watershed ridges, the catchment hillslopes, the tributary valleys—and the river.

Looking from the river across to either bank one sees a beginning, an edge to the vast blue-green of the rain forest beyond. The myth of the impenetrable jungle perhaps arose here. Here indeed there is a wall of dense, tangled, and often thorny vegetation. But it is a facade; it is the narrow strip of natural riverine (riparian) vegetation, and it displays a character and composition distinct from that of the tall and relatively open forest which it partially shields from view.

While roots within the forest spread wide and shallow, those of trees along the river banks must go deep, for anchorage. Along the river light is unrestricted. Tree trunks need not be tall and columnar; instead they tend to divide and spread to form a wide low crown, often leaning out and shading the water's edge. The alluvial soil along the large rivers is in places subject to erosion with every major flood. Banks are undercut and old trees topple; new banks build up and are colonised, first by hardy creeping plants and then perhaps by the upright plume-flowered elephant grasses.

Higher up the banks, wherever there is open space, plants of secondary forest and clearings invade to compete with the riverine trees and bamboos. As well as sunlight-demanding tree species there may sprout clumps of herbs such as gingers and wild aroids. At the boundary with the tall forest trees a curtain of climbing plants turns its leaves to the river's open brightness.

All this forms the habitat for animal life resident along the banks and dependent on the river and on riparian plants. It also provides a temporary home for migratory birds such as ospreys, sandpipers, barn swallows, and some bee-eaters.

When the first colonising agriculturalists came to tropical South-East Asia it was along the lower reaches of the rivers that the pioneer settlements were established. Population spread and now most rivers have cultivation all along the banks, often to the river's navigable limits and beyond. In many places boats still provide the only means of transport. Here and there along these yet remote waterways are places, perhaps even whole valleys, where the natural vegetation and wildlife of the river margin still remains.

Such a place is the Sungai Tembeling in Peninsular Malaysia, and the valley of its tributary Sungai Tahan. It is along these rivers that most of the photographs for this chapter were taken. The Tahan lies within a National Park, Taman Negara, and so is totally protected. The Tembeling, as part of the Park boundary, is afforded some protection; but domestic buffaloes—a vital source of livelihood for local people—are changing the face of the river margins wherever they browse and graze. Significant stretches, however, remain untouched—remnants of the vegetation that once stretched unbroken for 300 kilometres to the first brackish inroads of the sea.

The earliest adventurers moved up the rivers in dug-out canoes, poled and paddled against the flow. Nowadays, where still no roads serve upstream communities, outboard-motor longboats and diesel-engined express-boats ply the waters. Journeys by such means are memorable, and all the more so when there are roaring rapids to negotiate. But the most rewarding way to observe nature and absorb the unique atmosphere along a pristine stretch of river is to travel gently and silently by raft or canoe: the lapping, rippling water . . . the shrill ring of cicadas . . . the stare of a basking monitor lizard . . . and the exhilarating flash of cobalt blue from a kingfisher in sunlit flight!

4

Sungai Tembeling

Lagerstroemia speciosa Rose of India **Bungur** STP

The common and obvious plants along the banks of any large river in South-East Asia probably number no more than twenty different species, as against several hundred within the forest nearby. Because of quite different conditions for establishment and growth, few of these riverine species will be found within the forest proper, and few forest plants occur along the river banks. It is not difficult to recognise and learn the names of the riverside plants—such as the mauve-blossomed *Lagerstroemia* tree and the orange-petalled *Phanera* vine.

Bauhinia integrifolia GS

Trees and other riverine plants may be identified by their particular habit of growth, by their bark, by the distinctive shape or colour of their leaves, and, in season, by the character of their flowers or fruits.

Ficus racemosa (formerly named *F. glomerata*) Red river fig **Ara nasi** STP

Pometia pinnata **Kasai** STP

Eugenia densiflora var. *angustifolia* **Kelat jambu air**

Millettia hemsleyana **Jada** STP

Pterocymbium javanicum **Mata lembu**

Parkia javanica **Petai kerayung** STP

Gigantochloa wrayi

Daemonorops angustifolia A rattan **Rotan getah**

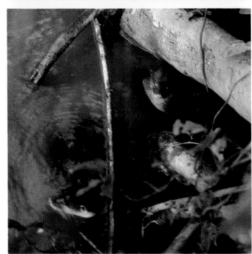

Amblonyx cinerea STP

Amblonyx cinerea Small-clawed otter **Memerang kecil**

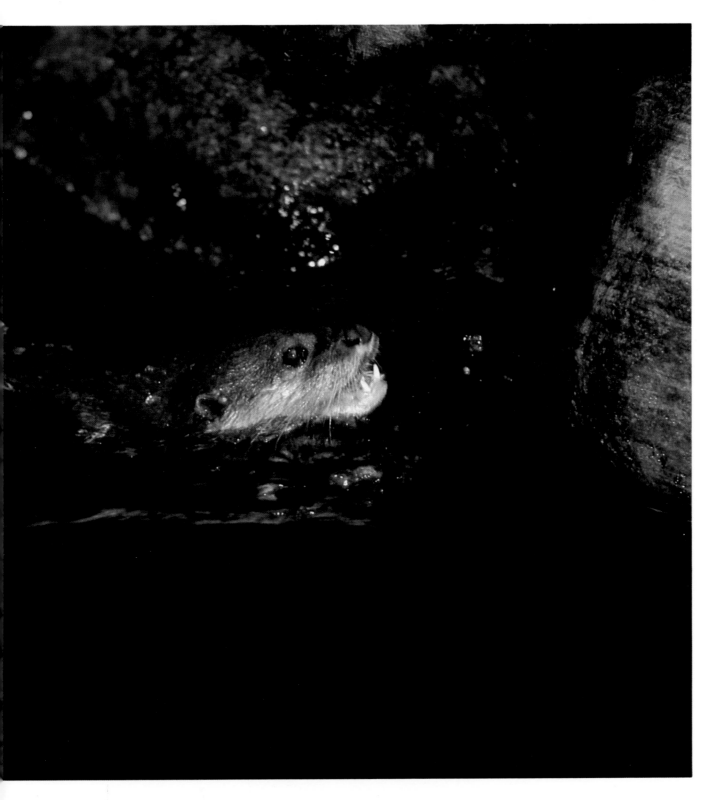

Of riverine wildlife, the small-clawed otter is only rarely seen. The species is widespread throughout South-East Asia, from river mouths to headwaters; but it is secretive in habits and shy when approached. Otters live in small family groups and are frolicsome animals moving efficiently and gracefully both in and out of the water. They feed on small fish, molluscs, and crustaceans.

In general, animal life seems unaccountably sparse along the big rivers, even along remote and little-disturbed stretches. An exception is the domestic buffalo which commonly invades the wild environment to graze wherever river banks are grassy. In turn, native animals of the river such as the water monitor lizard and the white-breasted kingfisher can sometimes be seen in and around riverine villages. Other wildlife is not so bold. The long-tailed macaque favours forested habitats near water, and may be glimpsed feeding on the fruits of riverside trees. The reclusive little green heron frequents shadowy nooks by the water's edge where it feeds on frogs, fish, and other forms of river life.

Macaca fascicularis Long-tailed macaque **Kera**

Varanus salvator Water monitor **Biawak air** STP

Butorides striatus Little green heron **Pucung keladi**

Pekaka/Raja udang STP

Halcyon smyrnensis White-throated kingfisher

Bos bubalis Water buffalo **Kerbau** STP

14

Tributaries slow to a near standstill where they enter the main river. But patterns of hidden currents may be revealed when, at the end of a flowering spate, the fallen petals of the riverbank *Millettia* tree (see also p. 8) form a carpet over the water's broad surface.

Kuala Pengau STP

Lubuk Simpon, Sungai Tahan

Even when flowing from a virgin forest catchment, a tropical river may run cloudy with silt after heavy rains. But in forest-bound tributaries the water soon regains its crystal clarity, and the boat-borne visitor can drift between pebbly sun-baked banks, or beneath a shady archway of giant **neram** trees, with the river bottom still visible two metres deep.

Dipterocarpus oblongifolius **Neram**, Sungai Tahan

Catopsilia pomona pomona

Python reticulatus Reticulated python **Ular sawa rendam** PT

Vestalis ?amoena A damselfly

?Libellago lineata A damselfly

Animal life along the tributaries may differ from that along the main river. Butterflies congregate on the sand, perhaps where some mammal has urinated. The python rests by day and hunts by night along the bank for frogs and larger animals. The damselfly is rarely far from water, emerging as a winged adult from its water-dwelling nymphal stage, to mate and then lay eggs in a river-edge pool. The box turtle, ideally equipped for passive self-defence, feeds both on land and in water on both vegetable matter and small animal life. It lays its eggs in a nest-hole dug in soft ground well above the water line.

Cuora amboinensis Malayan box turtle **Kura-kura**

Lubuk Simpon, Sungai Tahan

Morulius chrysophekadion **Ikan jengkua** STP

As with wildlife above the surface, different species of fish favour different habitats and different diets. Knowledge of these is of obvious advantage to the people who are dependent on the river for food. Fish of the carp family are common in South-East Asian rivers. Those such as **jengkua** and **kerai kunyit** favour larger rivers, while the **sebarau** prefers the fast-moving clear water of tributaries. Most carp are omnivorous, feeding on smaller fish, insect larvae, and tadpoles, as well as vegetable matter such as riverside fruits. The **kelesa** is unrelated to the carp. It is a carnivorous fish with close links to ancient fossil forms. **Sebarau** and **kelesa** can grow to more than 50 centimetres in length. Both are present in Sumatra, the Malay Peninsula, and Borneo. The **kelesa**, however, is a rare fish, and is scattered in occurrence; it favours deep pools in shady forest-bound tributaries.

Scleropages formosus Arowana **Ikan kelesa** C

Puntius daruphani **Kerai kunyit** STP

Hampala macrolepidota **Sebarau**

Dysoxylum angustifolium **Buah maris**

Eugenia densiflora var. angustifolia **Kelat jambu air**

Dipterocarpus oblongifolius **Neram**

Along the tributaries, riverside fruits are generally most abundant around mid-year. **Maris** and **jambu air** are small riverbank trees; **neram** is much larger; all three lean out over the water and their fruits and seeds fall and are carried downstream. The vivid red seeds of **maris** are highly valued as a fishing bait. Where **neram** trees occur, during the fruiting season their pink-winged fruits are conspicuous, whether hanging among the dark foliage, or fallen, stranded along the water's edge.

Daemonorops angustifolia A rattan **Rotan getah**

All climbing palms bear scaly fruits, and several species of the genus *Daemonorops* ("devil-bush") produce the flowers and fruits within distinctive spiny sheaths. **Rotan getah** is especially common along the borders of streams. How the seeds are distributed is uncertain.

Tristania whitiana **Pelawan**

Towards the upper reaches where the stream narrows and banks become rocky, the number of exclusively riverine plants dwindles, and trees of the forest extend right down to the river margin. But **pelawan** remains, an easily recognised smooth-barked tree related to the eucalypts of Australia. It occurs throughout tropical South-East Asia along rivers from their headwaters down to the tidal region. The tiny herb *Lindernia crustacea* is also wide-ranging, growing in rocky and sandy places from small tributaries all the way to the sea.

Lindernia crustacea BL

Lata Berkoh, Sungai Tahan

Sungai Atok

Every river has a character of its own defined by the terrain through which it flows, the geology of the area, the plants that line its banks, and perhaps even by its wildlife. The Sungai Tahan, in Pahang, Peninsular Malaysia, has its source in mountains above 2,000 metres where the peaty soil stains the water tea-brown. In the lowlands it cascades over sedimentary rocks in a steep-sided valley. The Sungai Atok is of an entirely different character, yet flows from a catchment neighbouring that of the Tahan. It is fed from a broad alluvial plain and meanders slowly along a deeply shaded course between high soil banks.

Ultimately the stream becomes part of the forest. From a boat at the navigable limit of a small river, tributaries that ripple and trickle from the forest offer a damp but relatively clear path in; so the journey may continue, on foot.

Tributary, Sungai Tahan

Stream on Gunung Macincang PL

STEPPING INT

Lowland tropical rain forest, Pahang, Peninsular Malaysia

THE FOREST

A Complex Structure

"A roof garden on pillars" ... "A great green cathedral" . . . "Verdant vaulted halls and gothic gloom" . . . So has the structure of the lowland rain forest been described. But is there really a scheme, a pattern, an architecture, to the way the tropical rain forest is built? To some degree there is: academic labels have been appended to different levels within the vegetation mass, from "A" for the crowns of the emergent trees down to "E" for the herbs and seedlings on the forest floor. In reality, in any patch of virgin lowland rain forest the emergent trees, commonly fifty or more metres tall, will certainly be obvious, and all the more so where they are spectacularly buttressed at the base; the rest of the forest, however, may well appear as a structural muddle.

It is nevertheless possible to describe in non-academic terms what parts make up the muddle. Below the emergent trees there is a more-or-less closed "roof" to the forest, give or take a few gaps here and there where large trees have fallen and new ones are beginning to grow up. This is the main canopy of the forest, the top of which, as might be seen in aerial view, is generally between 20 and 30 metres above the ground. The emergent trees tend to have crowns more broad than deep, often as much as 20 metres across; the trees of the main canopy, pressed side by side, have narrower, more rounded crowns.

Underneath this canopy, the amount of light that penetrates is dramatically reduced. Yet in this understorey a great deal grows, adapted to the low light conditions. Young trees and saplings striving to join the canopy have straight stems and high narrow crowns. Trees of species which are naturally small at maturity tend to have wider crowns, with the trunk branching out low down. Palms are often abundant in the understorey, adopting many forms, from stemless plants with a few small leaves to tree palms, some of which may eventually grow tall enough to form part of the canopy. From the forest floor itself sprout seedlings and, occasionally, attractively flowered forest herbs. Here, too, are fallen trunks, branches, twigs, and leaves, as well as the fungi that draw nutrients from them.

Within this framework, and adding further to the muddle, there are the opportunists: the climbers and the epiphytes. Trees expend a large proportion of available energy building supportive strength into their trunks. The largest climbers have leaf systems as extensive as those of the biggest trees; yet their stems, composed mainly of soft conducting tissues, can be severed with two strokes of a parang. The trees lend the energy-efficient climbers all the structural support they need.

One step further refined are the epiphytes, which shun all connection with the ground. They hitch a ride up in a tree fork or on a high branch, where the light is already bright. Though some are woody plants, none grows large. Their size is limited by the amount of moisture they can hold to carry them through rainless periods; but epiphytes can be great in individual numbers. Those best known are the orchids and the nest ferns.

The structure of the rain forest is not static. It is an architecture ever changing through growth and decay, yet in a state of overall equilibrium. What is today academically stratified, may tomorrow, in the perfectly natural course of events which causes a large tree to topple over, be a huge mess of debris.

Shorea leprosula **Meranti tembaga**

Dipterocarpus sp. **Keruing** GM

Trees with the dimensions of this specimen of *Shorea* (opposite) are commonplace in the virgin lowland rain forest of tropical South-East Asia. The columnar trunks of the tallest trees may rise 30 metres to the first branch, with the tops of their crowns occasionally 65 metres or more above ground. Trees of this stature are probably not less than 150 years old, and are thought to have a life-span of 300 years or more.

Root systems of large trees are often partially exposed, spreading wide and shallow rather than deep since nutrients are concentrated only in the thin surface layer of the soil. Many but not all of the dominant rain-forest trees develop wide buttresses as a result of the vertical development of the principal lateral roots; thus the trunk gains extra support.

Buttress development may be extreme in certain species such as *Tetrameles nudiflora.*

Tetrameles nudiflora **Mengkundur**

GS

In just a few square kilometres of lowland rain forest there may be four or five hundred different tree species present. Many of these would never be visible in an aerial view as they are shade-tolerant species which at maturity do not reach the level of the main canopy. This canopy is formed by light-demanding species. A few such species, commonly representatives of the dipterocarp and legume families (see p. 74) grow to become dominant (emergent) trees standing "head and shoulders" above the others.

From beneath, it is evident that the leaves of emergent trees, main-canopy trees, and large climbing plants intercept a very large proportion of the direct sunlight, leaving the forest floor in semi-darkness.

Myrialepis paradoxa (formerly named *M. scortechinii*) **Rotan kertung**

The trees of the lowland rain forest form the main structure within which plants of other growth habits fill particular niches. Climbing plants are an example, and are strongly characteristic of tropical rain forest. Notable among these are the climbing palms or rattans. The mature leaves of most species of rattans have the midrib greatly extended beyond the leaflets. This midrib is armed with sharp hooks. The slender stem grows upwards but soon topples sideways. The hooks check the fall by catching onto adjacent vegetation; and so, step by step, the palm "climbs" into the canopy.

Lianas climb more directly, spiralling upwards around slender tree trunks, other lianas, or even their own stems (right). Many grow thick and woody with age, and may develop sufficient foliage to retard significantly the growth of their supporting tree or trees. At the lower levels, climbing herbs are present, twining among the undergrowth or creeping on tree trunks (below).

N.I.

Also characteristic of tropical rain-forest structure is an abundance of epiphytes. These are not parasites but simply use other plants as a permanent "perch", so that they can grow in places well exposed to the light. If they fall to the dimness of the forest floor, they die.

The most conspicuous epiphytes are ferns (right). These take firm root in a crevice in the bark of a tree. As they grow, many species develop a basket of leaves within which fine debris and moisture gather to facilitate the plant's further growth. Epiphytic plants survive only because of the year-round rainfall and high humidity of the rain forest. A great many orchids grow as epiphytes, but so high up in the canopy as to be rarely seen in the lowlands.

Algae and mosses, and (below) lichens and liverworts, are abundant as tiny epiphytes growing on bark, rocks, and even on old leaves.

Platycerium holttumii Stag's horn fern **Paku tanduk rusa** C

Asplenium nidus Bird's nest fern **Paku pandan** BL

Ficus sp.

The most bizarre element in the rain-forest structure is the strangling fig. Several species are common throughout the lowlands and hills. The seed of the fig is deposited on a tree branch in the droppings of a bird or arboreal mammal. Here it germinates and sends fine roots down, usually via the trunk. These roots enter the soil, thicken, divide, and rejoin around the tree trunk. Meanwhile, the fig develops an extensive crown of leafy branches which compete for light with the leaves of the host tree. Ultimately, the host may die from inadequate light and constriction of the conducting vessels in the trunk; if the trunk rots away completely the fig is left standing independently on its own hollow latticework stem (opposite).

Ficus sp.

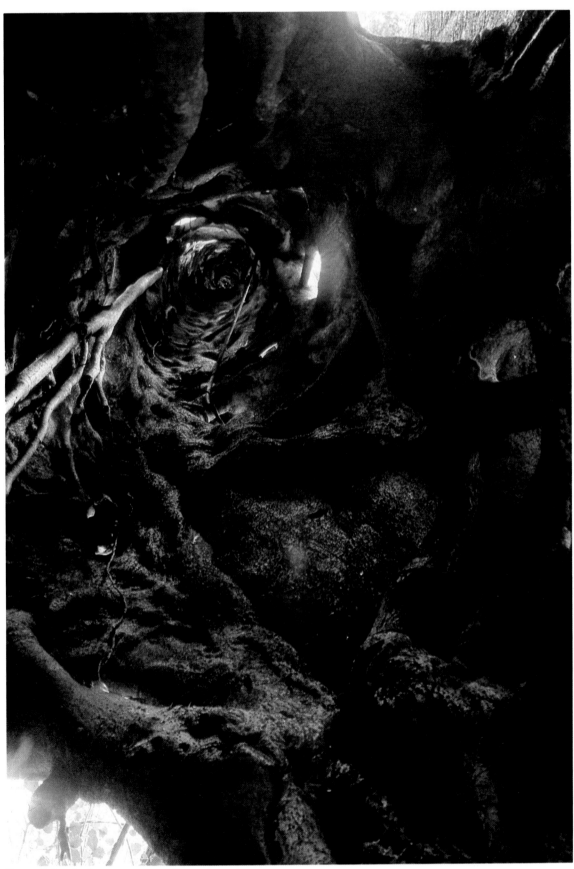

Ficus sp. A strangling fig

Pholidocarpus macrocarpus **Kepau**

The undergrowth of the tropical rain forest is the nursery for the seedlings and saplings of the tall forest trees, as well as the favoured habitat of many plants that will never reach up to the canopy level. Palms of many kinds thrive in this dimly lit environment. Some, like *Pholidocarpus macrocarpus* (main picture), appear first as a stemless palm, but ultimately develop a trunk (like that of a coconut palm), and reach a height of 15 metres or more.

Caryota mitis **Tukas** TLB

Calamus castaneus **Cucur**

Caryota mitis (upper right) develops one or more slender stems two to three metres tall. Many palm species, however, remain stemless with long leaves radiating out from ground level, as in *Calamus castaneus* (lower right). In shape, palm leaves may be simple (with an unbroken margin), forked, or much-divided in the pattern of a feather, a fan, or fish tails.

Didymocarpus platypus (purple form) GBB

At the lowest structural level, beneath the undergrowth, forest herbs may be found, many just a few centimetres tall. Such plants are present in both lowland and hill forest but are very patchily distributed. Most flower for only a few weeks of the year.

Many herb species have distinctive leaf or floral characteristics, and as such are among the easier forest plants to recognise and identify (see overleaf).

Didymocarpus atrosanguineus

Phyllagathis scortechinii

Didymocarpus ?vandaalenii BL

Tacca ?integrifolia **Janggut baung** GL

Philodendron sp. STP

Pentaphragma horsfieldii (formerly named *P. scortechinii*)

Phyllagathis rotundifolia **Akar serau malam**

Globba ?patens

Pavetta sp.

Trentepohlia aurea Of the green algae group GT

Ulothrix sp. and *Phormidium* sp. Filamentous green, and blue-green, algae

The algae are an ancient group of plants which existed in the sea more than 500 million years ago, before the first land plants came into being. Today, seaweeds are the best-known algae. There are also many non-marine species, but these are tiny plants which to be appreciated fully need to be viewed under a microscope. In the rain forest, green filamentous algae (above) may be found in clear running water. Damp ground supports a variety of algal forms such as the orange *Trentepohlia* (opposite), which also grows on tree trunks and even on leaves. Like the large green plants of the forest, most algae contain chlorophyll; and so, given sunlight, carbon dioxide, and water, they can photosynthesise their own materials for growth.

Most bacteria have no chlorophyll. Many cause the rotting of dead material, and so obtain soluble nutrients directly. In the rain forest, fine particles of dead plant matter gather in still water at stream edges; here filamentous bacteria thrive, forming an orange-brown sludge.

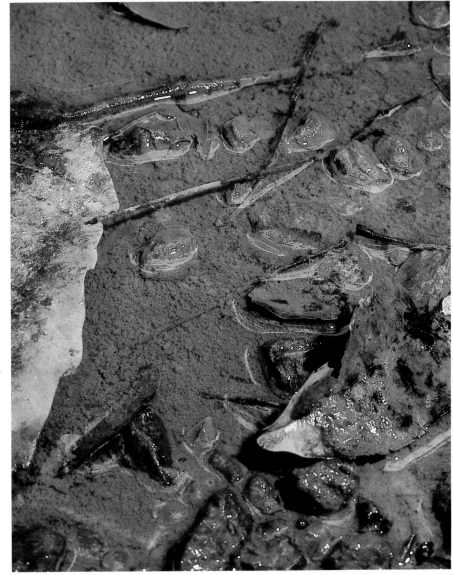

N.I. Filamentous bacteria

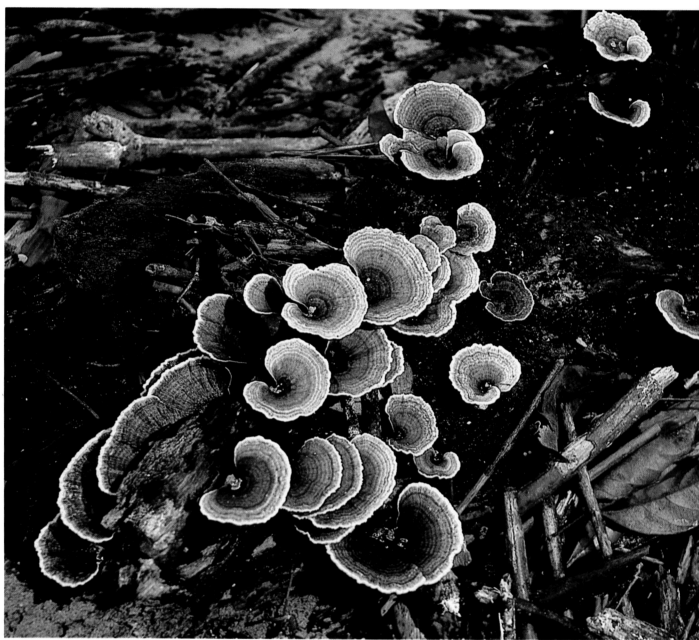

N.I. (?Polyporaceae)

Fungi, like the algae, mosses, and ferns, reproduce and spread by spores, with an intermediate growth stage leading to the development of the new plant. Fungi do not contain chlorophyll, but derive the energy they need for growth by breaking down the tissues of other plants—commonly dead wood. Thus the fungi act as valuable agents of decay in the forest and serve to recycle nutrients.

N.I. (?Polyporaceae)

Cookeina tricholoma (Sarcoscyphaceae) A cup fungus TLB

Usually it is only the spore-producing reproductive parts of the fungus that are seen in the rain forest. These occur in a great variety of shapes, sizes, and colours; but for identification even into a broad category (bracket fungus, coral fungus, puff-ball etc.) the outward appearance serves as no more than a rough guide. For positive identification of species, it is often necessary to examine microscopically the spores or spore-producing organs of the fungus.

Microporus xanthopus (Polyporaceae) A bracket fungus

58

Identifications:

Malay names:
cendawan for mushrooms and toadstools, **kulat** for bracket fungi.

1. *Clavulinopsis* sp. (Clavariaceae) A coral fungus
2. *Cyathus* sp. (Nidulariaceae) A bird's nest fungus
3. *Heimiella* sp. (Boletaceae)
4. *Lentinus velutinus* (Tricholomataceae)
5. *Scleroderma* sp. (Sclerodermataceae) A puff ball
6. *Xylaria* sp. (Xylariaceae)
7. *Mycena* sp. (Tricholomataceae)
8. *Mycena ?manipularis* (Tricholomataceae)
9. *Pycnoporus coccineus* (Polyporaceae) A bracket fungus
10. *Lentinus* sp. (Tricholomataceae)
11. *?Dacrymyces* sp. (Tremellales) A jelly fungus
12. *Cystoderma* sp. (Tricholomataceae)
13. *Coprinus* sp. (Coprinaceae)
14. N.I.
15. *Termitomyces* sp. (Tricholomataceae)
16. N.I. (?Polyporaceae)
17. *Lentinus* sp. (Tricholomataceae)
18. *Hygrophorus* sp. (Hygrophoraceae)

Lichens occur in abundance in the rain forest. They may be present as a pale encrustation on the bark of trees and on the surface of old leaves (p. 40, left); they may be foliose (leaf-like) creeping on bark or rock, perhaps in company with liverworts (right) or mosses; or they may be stalked and branched (below), on tree branches or rock. A lichen arises from the mutually beneficial (symbiotic) partnership that can develop between a fungus and an alga, and so functions as two-plants-in-one. Lichens are slow-growing, but hardy and long-living.

Cladonia sp. GT

N.I. Lichens and a liverwort GS

GUK

?Vesicularia sp. A bladder moss

Pogonatum junghuhnianum GK

The mosses and the closely related liverworts appear to be descended from the algae. Like the algae, mosses are dependent on water for the sexual phase of their reproduction, and thus are generally confined to damp and shady habitats. Mosses are most abundant in the forest of high mountain ridges (opposite), but are also widespread in the lowlands, growing in soil, and on bark, leaves, and decaying logs. Whereas the higher plants develop true roots, stems, and leaves, similar-looking parts of the moss are in fact much simpler structures. Mosses rarely contain any specialised cells for the transport of water and food material, and so they do not develop woody tissues or grow to large size. New plants develop through dissemination of spores produced in tiny capsules (left).

Lycopodium cernuum A club moss GT

Selaginella wildenovii Peacock plant **Paku merak**

Among the first members of the plant kingdom to have passages within their tissues for transport of food and water around the plant were the club-mosses. *Lycopodium* (upper left) is a common example. It grows on waste land in the lowlands, and also in the mountain forests. Its creeping branching stem may grow to two metres or more in length. Similar plants have been found in fossils 280 million years old.

Closely related to the club-mosses is *Selaginella wildenovii* (lower left). It is a widespread herb of the lowland-forest understorey. The surface cells of the primitive leaves reflect green or blue according to the angle of view.

Both *Selaginella* and *Lycopodium* reproduce by spores arising in cone-like structures which develop at the ends of the stems.

Cyathea sp. A tree fern FH

Ferns are able to grow in almost any tropical environment, from coastal swamps to high mountains. In the lowland rain forest, terrestrial ferns grow along the banks of streams (previous page); there are epiphytic ferns such as *Drynaria* and *Platycerium* on the branches and trunks of trees; and there are slender climbing ferns. In the mountains there is the tree fern *Cyathea* with stems three or more metres tall; on exposed sites the hardy sun-loving *Matonia* and *Dipteris* ferns (pp. 184—5) may occur; and in many moist sheltered places the delicate filmy ferns such as *Trichomanes* can be found. Scourge of open ground in the lowlands and hills is the tough and fast-growing **resam** fern, *Gleichenia*.

Unlike mosses, ferns bear true roots and leaves. The stem in many fern species is long and somewhat woody, extending horizontally either underground as in *Gleichenia* or across the surface as in *Drymoglossum* and *Pyrrosia*, and termed a rhizome. Such species may colonise new territory by extension of the rhizome.

All ferns establish new plants through the agency of wind-borne spores which develop in minute capsules called sporangia. A cluster of sporangia is termed a sorus, and these are visible either on the underside of the fern leaves, as in *Microsorium, Pronephrium,* and others, or on special reproductive shoots such as those of *Platycerium.* The mode of arrangement of these sori is a valuable guide in the identification of ferns.

Drynaria quercifolia **Daun kelapa tupai**

Platycerium coronarium Stag's horn fern

Paku tanduk rusa GS

Trichomanes bipunctatum A filmy fern G

Gleichenia truncata **Resam** BL

(formerly genus *Phymatodes*)

Microsorium nigrescens **Paku ciai/Paku sumpah**

Pronephrium repandum (formerly named *Abacopteris urophylla*)

Pyrrosia adnascens **Sakat batu** KGR

Drymoglossum piloselloides **Sisik naga** GS

Cycas sp. A cycad **Paku agi** C

Gnetum ?ridleyi

The group of non-flowering plants called the Gymnosperma ("naked seed" bearers) has few representatives in the tropics. *Cycas* has an appearance similar to that of the tree ferns. Its plants are either male or female; the male develops huge cones, producing pollen, while the female (left) develops special seed-bearing shoots. *Cycas* grows in lowland rain forest, more commonly in coastal areas. *Gnetum* species are almost entirely climbing plants. Some, with thick woody climbing stems and marked nodal ridges, are quite common in lowland forest. From the nodes arise male or female reproductive shoots, the latter producing the exposed seeds (above). A major group within the gymnosperms is the conifers (cone-bearing plants), representatives of which, in tropical South-East Asia, are mainly confined to the mountains. *Agathis borneensis* (opposite) is a large tree of the hill forest with an easily recognisable bark and distinctive fallen cones; *Dacrydium* (p. 188) is also a conifer.

Agathis borneensis (formerly named *A. dammara*) **Damar minyak** GJ

The flowering plants have, as a group, evolved most recently—within the last 140 million years. They are by far the most numerous and dominant plants of the tropical rain forest. Contrary to popular opinion, very few flowers of the rain forest are bright and showy. Small pale flowers are the norm since most utilise scent rather than form or colour to attract pollinating agents, mainly insects. Forest trees tend to be very variable in their intensity of flowering, and there are some species which go through several years without flowering at all. **Tualang** trees flower particularly heavily (right) one year in perhaps five or six, producing a carpet of pollen on the forest floor from millions of tiny wind-pollinated flowers. In the lowland rain forest, widespread, heavy, and synchronous flowering seems to occur at least once every decade, associated with the onset of good rains following an unusually severe dry season.

Koompassia excelsa **Tualang**

Saraca thaipingensis **Gapis** C

Hibiscus floccosus **Kangsar**

Polyalthia sp.

A few forest trees—mostly smaller ones—do produce handsome flowers, thought in some cases, such as *Hibiscus* (lower left), to attract birds rather than insects as pollinators. Wild *Hibiscus* blooms are short-lived, remaining open on the tree only a day or two before the flower-head falls, whereas those of *Saraca* (top) maintain their richly colourful display for more than a week before they wither and fall.

A characteristic of tropical rain forest is the tendency for some trees, usually understorey species, to bear flowers and fruits on the trunk and branches as in *Polyalthia* (opposite) and *Saraca* (right), rather than from the leafy shoots. Termed cauliflory, this strategy may enable utilisation of quite different species of insects (or other kinds of animals) as agents of pollination, from those employed by canopy-flowering plants.

Saraca trees may grow almost like an avenue alongside small streams, where their flowers and their vividly coloured pods make a spectacular show in season. Distinctive in a quite different way are the pods of the deciduous *Intsia palembanica* (overleaf). At maturity these turn black on the tree at a time when the branches are altogether bare awaiting the flush of new leaf growth.

Saraca thaipingensis **Gapis**

Intsia palembanica **Merbau**

Dipterocarpus costulatus **Keruing kipas** C

Parkia javanica **Petai kerayung**

Of as many as 200 different species of trees on any single hectare of lowland rain forest in South-East Asia, a third might belong to a single family of plants, the Dipterocarpaceae or dipterocarps. The name means "two-winged fruit". This is perfectly exemplified in the helicopter fruits of *Dipterocarpus* (above left); but others in the family have fruits that are wingless, or with three, four, or five wings.

The only other family to seriously challenge the dipterocarps in terms of numbers of tall-tree species is that of the legumes, Leguminosae. The fruits of this family usually take the form of a pod. Examples are *Parkia* (above right) and *Saraca* (p. 71). **Merbau** (previous page) and **tualang** (pp. 68–9) are dominant trees in some lowland forest areas; both are legumes.

Pure stands of a single tree species are virtually unknown in the lowland forest. But there are places on ridge-crests in hill forest where the tall dipterocarp *Shorea curtisii* commands the scene, its lofty blue-grey crowns contrasting clearly with those of other tree species.

Grey crowns: *Shorea curtisii* **Seraya** GS

Sterculia ?coccinea **Kelumpang**

Sindora echinocalyx **Sepetir daun nipis**

Dysoxylum cauliflorum

Durio zibethinus Durian **Durian** C

Flowering plants are customarily identified by reference to their flowers and fruits. But in the tropical rain forest, flowering is irregular and infrequent in many species; fresh flowers and fruits of forest trees are generally high up, beyond easy reach; and most fallen fruits decompose rapidly. Rain-forest botanists have therefore learned to identify tree species from their fallen leaves, and by the cut surface and external appearance of the bark. Nevertheless, when fruits are present they are often distinctive in form, colour, or texture; and the **durian** is absolutely unmistakable in flavour!

Calamus paspalanthus A rattan

Rotan sirikis

Eugeissona brachystachys

Bertam Tahan

Pinanga malaiana **Legung**

In the rain forest, palms form a sizeable component of the flowering-plant community and can often be found bearing fruit. The principal aids to palm identification are the flowers, the fruits, and the structure of the leaves.

According to the presence of one or two primary leaves (cotyledons) in the seed, botanists classify all flowering plants as either monocotyledons or dicotyledons. Forest trees—tree palms excepted—are all in the latter category. The gingers and orchids (following pages), as well as grasses (including bamboos) and palms, are all examples of monocotyledons.

Achasma triorgyale GS

No family of South-East Asian rain-forest plants produces flowers more richly and variously coloured than those of the ginger family, Zingiberaceae (left and overleaf). Gingers are herbs of the forest floor. Most species develop a long underground stem from which arise individual leaf-bearing stems, in some cases three or more metres tall. The leaves are much longer than broad, and grow out from each side of the stem (or, in the case of the genus *Costus*, spirally); they are fragrant when crushed. The flower-bearing shoot may arise directly from the underground stem as in *Achasma*, so appearing out of the soil with no obvious connection to the leaves; or it may develop on the leafy stem as in *Costus* and *Alpinia*. Many gingers seem to thrive best on disturbed sites, or at the forest edge along rivers and around clearings.

Amomum aculeatum

Costus speciosus

Achasma megalocheilos

Zingiber spectabile **Tepus tanah**

Nicolaia speciosa (formerly genus *Phaeomeria*) Torch ginger **Bunga kantan**

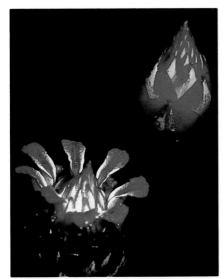

Nicolaia maingayi (formerly genus *Phaeomeria*)

Achasma megalocheilos (variegated form, formerly named *A. macrocheilos*)

Alpinia rafflesiana

Coelogyne cumingii

Tainia sp.

Phreatia secunda GS

The orchids, in their floral structure, are the most advanced of all flowering plants, and also among the most distinctive. Sepals and petals often appear similar as in *Coelogyne* (opposite), except for the lowermost petal, the lip, which is usually complex in shape. In almost all orchids the pollen is borne on a single stamen, and this is united with the female parts, the stigma and style. This combined structure—called the column—is ingeniously adapted to facilitate the transfer by insects of clusters of pollen grains from the stamen of one flower to the stigma of another of the same species, for cross-fertilisation.

While some orchids, such as *Tainia* (top left), are terrestrial plants, the majority grow as epiphytes. *Dendrobium* (centre) and the tiny *Phreatia* (top right) are epiphytic on tree branches; *Bulbophyllum* (bottom) was found creeping on rock.

Most epiphytic orchids develop pseudobulbs. These are markedly swollen stem bases (clearly displayed on *Bulbophyllum skeateanum*, p. 193) and serve as water storage organs, as do the thick fleshy leaves present in many orchid species.

Orchids occur world-wide, but are most abundant in the tropics, especially in the mountain forest. On Sabah's Gunung Kinabalu alone there are at least 700 species of orchids.

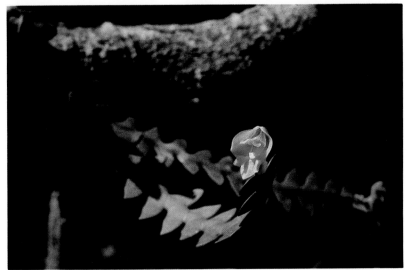

Dendrobium sp.

Bulbophyllum ?nigrescens

Animal Life of the Rain Forest

Most people are aware that there is an abundance of wildlife in the tropical rain forest. But who has managed to see it? By day at least, the visitor can expect to encounter very few mammals beyond a squirrel or two and, with luck, a fleeting glimpse of monkeys. There might be a hundred or more species of birds about but the novice, while hearing plenty, will likely obtain a good clear view of hardly any. Snakes, venomous or otherwise, are very rarely seen. Solitary butterflies momentarily appear, and disappear; cicadas are much heard but little seen; even mosquitoes tend to be few in virgin rain forest. If little is to be observed in the lowlands, even less will be seen in the mountains.

The story can be altogether different should one travel in the company of an expert. An experienced bird-watcher will probably spot 60 to 80 species in the first day in lowland forest, and double that tally in a week. Someone who knows where to look might uncover, in the space of a few hours, a dozen kinds of snake or scores of different beetles or spiders. Those in search of mammals, or frogs, will go out at night with a torchlight. It all takes a trained eye, practice, patience and enthusiasm.

People generally like to be able to identify the wildlife they see. Description of form and plumage suffices for birds. Squirrels are straightforward too. But there are many other animals which one must have in the hand if positive identification is to be made: snakes—to count certain scales and observe their arrangement; bats—to examine their teeth; rats—to check their nipples and measure their feet; frogs—to inspect their teeth, tongue, tympanum, tubercles, toes. Identification of some moths requires dissection of the genitalia under a microscope. Most people, quite understandably, get no further than the commoner birds. Regular visitors to the rain forest, however, can hardly help being stimulated to deeper involvement. But it is difficult to know where to start.

The animal kingdom is so diverse it can be divided up in many ways. The photographs following are set out in the generally accepted order of evolution of the animal groups covered. This section is biased towards animals active by day (diurnal) with the nocturnal ones appearing in a later section. Food preferences could be another means of categorisation: carnivores (tigers, praying mantids), herbivores (deer, stick insects), and those that eat both meat and vegetable matter, the omnivores (wild pigs, cockroaches).

The animals could also be classified according to their favoured habitat. The tropical rain forest provides a great variety of niches. In the soil—cicada nymphs, termites, burrowing snakes; on the forest floor—the ubiquitous leech, millipedes, pheasants, mousedeer; in the undergrowth and lower canopy—butterflies, tree frogs, gliding lizards, woodpeckers, smaller squirrels; in the upper canopy—bees, leaf-feeding insects, hornbills, large squirrels, fruit bats, gibbons; and above the canopy—high-flying insects, swifts, nightjars, eagles, insectivorous bats.

Of rain-forest animals habitually aggressive and dangerous to humans, there is really only one—the hornet. The worst kind seems to nest in the ground. When disturbed (and instances are uncommon) they attack fiercely and without warning. A good defence is to run, and a better one to run faster.

Of animals just habitually aggressive, none compares with the leech. It is harmless, and can best be removed by calmly and gently easing it off with a fingernail.

Nephila maculata FH

Haemadipsa sp. A land leech **Pacat**

The tropical rain forest of South-East Asia has been evolving, without catastrophic interruption, for more than 100 million years. It seems likely that throughout this time the forest has been the home of the leech. Leeches are parasitic animals of the forest floor, and they feed on mammalian blood. There is a sucker at each end of the body; that at the head end surrounds the mouth-parts comprising three saw-like teeth. Upon finding a host, the leech punctures the skin and injects into the blood an anti-coagulant. The leech may then absorb several times its own body weight in blood before dropping off. One meal may last six months or more. Leeches are an occupational hazard to human travellers in the rain forest, but their bite is painless and they transmit no disease.

A soft-bodied animal like the leech has only its camouflage for protection against predation; another, the snail (p. 138), is also of ancient origins but has progressed a step by developing a hard shell into which it can quickly withdraw from danger. Then came a major advance, in the evolution of the Arthropoda. The name means "joint-legged"; but the most obvious feature of this group is the presence of a tough segmented external skeleton. Thus the animal has some degree of permanent protection. Millipedes, centipedes, crabs, spiders, and insects are familiar arthropods.

Millipedes are vegetable-feeders, foraging on the forest floor and in the soil. If threatened, they increase the effectiveness of their armour-plating by rolling up into a tight spiral—an art most highly refined in the pill millipede (bottom).

Platyrachus sp. GS

Thyropygus pachyurus BL

?Sphaeropoeus sp. A pill millipede GS

88

Scolopendra sp. **Lipan** GS

N.I. GS

Palamnaeus sp. **Kala bangkang** GS

Notable predators among the rain forest's non-insect arthropods are the centipedes, scorpions, and spiders. In the arthropods, evolutionary advance is displayed in reduction in the number of walking legs, and in division of the body into specialised sections (head, thorax, and abdomen in the insects). The millipede has two pairs of legs per body segment; the centipede, one. The front legs of the centipede are modified into poison fangs. In the scorpion the front segments are fused, and the final segment bears the poison gland and sting; there are eight walking legs, with a further pair modified to form the pincers. The spider also has eight appendages for walking; a further pair (the pedipalps) acts as feelers, and between these there is a pair adapted to serve as poison fangs.

The insects form by far the largest subdivision of the arthropods. Insects never have more than three pairs of legs. Among the most advanced insects are members of a group called the Hymenoptera ("membranous-winged"), including wasps (and hornets), bees, and ants. The females of most wasps and bees carry a sting at the end of the abdomen, as do some ant species—notably several kinds of ground-dwelling "fire ants" (below). All ants, and some wasps (right) and bees (overleaf), are social insects, living in communities in which the larvae are fed and cared for by the adult insects. Any human disturbance to such communities may provoke swift and painful retaliation!

Polybia orientalis A communal wasp **Penyengat**

N.I. Fire ant **Semut api**

Two kinds of bees are readily observed in the rain forest, since both tend to be attracted to human sweat. This is especially so of the small stingless *Trigona* bees (below), which build their nest in a hollow tree, and construct from wax an elegant entrance tube. The giant honey bee *Megapis dorsata* is a stinging species which may occur in the forest in audibly huge numbers during years of especially heavy flowering. Large nests are built suspended beneath branches of tall trees, especially **tualang** trees (right).

Oecophylla smaragdina Weaving ant **Kerengga** GS

Trigona sp. Sweat bee **Kelulut**

Macrotermes carbonarius (mound)

Macrotermes carbonarius (queen)

The weaving ant is present in tropical gardens as well as in the rain forest, and is well known for its readiness to deliver a sharp bite with its powerful mandibles. Its nest is built by drawing together, and fixing with silken threads, the leaves of a living tree.

Macrotermes carbonarius

Termites are unrelated to ants. Termites generally build their nests in the soil, making huge mounds in the case of *Macrotermes carbonarius* (see also pp. 130–1). In both ants and termites, the community within the nest is divided into several castes, from the king and the hugely expanded egg-laying queen, to workers, soldiers, and potential reproductives of both sexes. Within their nests, termites (and many ants) cultivate fungus for food (left).

While ants reproduce through complete metamorphosis (egg, larva, pupa, adult), the termites are more primitive insects with the young hatching directly from the egg, and developing by a series of progressive growth stages (incomplete metamorphosis) into the various castes of adults.

Cryptotympanum aquila A cicada **Riang-riang** GS

Insects evolved from centipede-like ancestors, and the capacity for flight developed very early. The structure and arrangement of wings is an important feature in the classification of insects into orders and sub-orders, as is the mode of development from egg to adult.

The adult cicada (opposite), having two near-identical pairs of wings, is placed in the sub-order Homoptera ("alike-winged"). Cicada eggs hatch into tiny nymphs which burrow into the soil. The nymphs have a life span of several years, and develop by progressive moults. At the time for the final moult the still-wingless insect tunnels up from the soil (mud-tube, right) and attaches itself to a tree trunk. The skin is split and the winged adult emerges, leaving behind the old exoskeleton (far right).

Adult male cicadas are responsible for the sustained and penetrating "singing" heard at various times throughout the day in the rain forest.

Tiarodes sp. An assassin bug

Related to the cicadas are the bugs, commonly termed stink-bugs for the strong odour they emit if molested. Here the front part of the fore-wings is thickened and opaque, providing a hard protective layer. The majority of insects have biting mouth-parts, but the bugs, cicadas, and related insects have evolved a tube-like proboscis for piercing tissues and sucking out the juice. Cicada nymphs feed on tree roots. The nymphs and adults of most bugs feed on leaves and soft stems, but an exception is the predatory assassin bug (mating, left) which feeds mainly on other insects.

94

Cethosia hypsea hypsina FH

Paralaxita damajanti damajanti

Euploea diocletianus diocletianus

Mycalesis mineus macromalayana

Psaphis euschymoides javanicus

The Lepidoptera ("scale-winged" insects) comprise the moths and butterflies. There are perhaps 1,500 species of butterflies in South-East Asia. Almost all fly by day—as do some moths, such as *Psaphis* (opposite, bottom left). Butterflies are a fairly common sight in both lowland and hill forest at any time of the year. Many species visit flowers to feed on nectar; they may also be attracted to salt-licks, decaying fruit, carrion, animal excrement, or sweaty clothing.

The caterpillars of almost all butterflies feed on plant tissue; most species are restricted to just one kind of plant, or in some instances to a few closely related kinds. A butterfly lays eggs, singly or grouped, on the surface of a leaf of the food plant. The hatched caterpillar (larva) has biting mouth-parts and feeds voraciously. It grows rapidly through several stages, shedding the old skin at each. After the final moult the skin of the caterpillar hardens to form the case of the pupa (chrysalis), which in most species is suspended by threads from a twig. Inside the pupal case the tissues of the caterpillar are reorganised. Usually after two or three weeks the adult (imago) emerges. In an hour or so the butterfly's wings expand and harden, whereupon it can fly off in search of a mate.

Butterflies, in total contrast to their larvae, have sucking mouth-parts in the form of an extendable coiled proboscis.

In moths (see pp. 146–7) the life history follows a pattern very similar to that of the butterflies. Moth larvae, however, usually either spin a cocoon (p. 147) or pupate in the soil. In contrast with butterflies, most moths are active only at night and tend to rest with their wings held flat. The antennae of butterflies are club-shaped; those of moths may be of various shapes in different species, but are commonly feather-like.

Egg, larva, chrysalis, and imago ♀ of *Papilio memnon agenor* GS

96

Vertebrate animals (those with a backbone) have evolved along a quite separate path from the invertebrates. The first vertebrates, some 500 million years ago, were fish-like creatures. From these evolved amphibious animals—the predecessors of the frogs. Of more than 150 species of frogs and toads in the South-East Asian rain forest, most still require water for spawning and for the development of the tadpoles. But the eggs of some tree frogs such as *Polypedates* (right) develop in the absence of water, in a foam mass suspended from vegetation over a stream or pool. On hatching, the tadpoles drop into the water below.

Polypedates colletti Hour-glass bush frog

katak pokok potongan

Geochelone emys (formerly genus *Testudo*) Burmese brown tortoise **Baning**

From amphibian ancestors, the first reptiles appeared about 300 million years ago, and from these have evolved the tortoises and turtles, the crocodiles, the lizards, and the snakes.

A forest-dwelling tortoise 50 million years ago probably looked much like the present-day Burmese brown tortoise (opposite). Its shell is formed of bony plates fused with the backbone and ribs, and the limbs, head, and tail are retractable. This species can grow to half a metre in length and more than 30 kilograms in weight. It is mainly vegetarian, but also feeds on carrion.

Of rain-forest lizards, it is the fleet-footed skinks (right) that are most frequently encountered, often warming themselves in a patch of sunlight. Skinks feed mainly on insects, and the largest species grow to about 25 centimetres. The monitor lizards (lower right, and p. 12) are represented by at least four species in Sumatra, the Malay Peninsula, and Borneo. The largest is the water monitor, growing to about two metres. Monitors are carnivorous animals, and scavengers. Some species climb readily and are known to take eggs from birds' nests—and village hen-houses!

All reptiles lay eggs, though in some species of vipers these are retained within the snake's body until the young hatch. Crocodiles and a few species of snakes guard their eggs during incubation, but in most reptiles the eggs are left unattended.

Dasia olivacea A skink **Bengkarung**

Varanus rudicollis Harlequin monitor lizard **Biawak serunai**

Trimeresurus hageni Hagen's pit viper GS

Of more than 100 species of land and freshwater snakes in the South-East Asian rain forest, most, like the bronze-back tree snake (previous page), are harmless to all except the small animal life on which they feed. Fewer than 20 species have a venomous bite, and only that of the cobras and kraits—and in rare instances the coral snakes and the vipers—can be fatal to humans.

In the rain forest there are water snakes, burrowing snakes, ground snakes, and tree snakes. The smallest grow to no more than pencil-size. The region's largest snake is the reticulated python (p. 18), which commonly grows to four metres and has been recorded at more than twice that length.

Snakes are predominantly nocturnal and possess unusual sensory equipment. They are deaf to airborne sounds but sensitive to ground vibrations. The forked tongue connects to a special organ in the roof of the mouth, so that they detect scents by "tasting". The pit vipers (right) have in addition a pair of unique heat-sensitive organs. Each is located in a hollow—the pit—between the eye and the nostril, and together they enable the snake to precisely locate warm-blooded prey.

Trimeresurus wagleri Wagler's pit viper **Ular kapak tokong**

A few species of rain-forest tree snakes can glide to some degree by compressing their bodies to form a hollow underneath. The flying gecko (p. 156) also has a limited capacity to glide. But neither remotely approaches the gliding efficiency of the "flying dragon", *Draco*. Stationary on a tree trunk it is almost invisible; only in flight is it obvious. Within the foldable gliding membrane are muscle-adjustable supports, developed through modification of some of the rib bones. The lizard can manoeuvre in mid-air, and from high on one tree trunk can land gently and precisely at the base of another 30 metres away. The wing structure is however altogether different from that of a bird or bat; *Draco* can glide, and frequently does, but it cannot fly.

Above and right: *Draco melanopogon* Gliding lizard **Kubin** GS

Anthracoceros convexus Southern pied hornbill **Enggang kelingking**

Pycnonotus goiavier Yellow-vented bulbul **Merbah** GS

Napothera macrodactyla Large wren babbler

True flight is limited to the insects, the birds, and the bats. The first of the bird-like animals evolved about 150 million years ago, from small lizard-like reptilians. These were not cold-blooded like other reptiles, but warm-blooded; and feathers, which arose through development from scales, provided useful insulation. Birds now form the largest group of vertebrate animals.

Among the biggest, noisiest, and most unmistakable birds of the South-East Asian region, are the hornbills (opposite). There are several species. They are most remarkable for their nesting habits. The male seals the female into a nest-hole in a hollow tree, blocking the entrance with mud, except for a small crack through which he feeds his mate throughout the laying and incubation period. Only when the young are so large as to require extra feeding, does the female break out.

Much more conventional is the babbler (left), relying on cryptic colouring for concealment of bird and nest.

Newly hatched bulbuls (opposite) are typical of the young of most forest birds, being initially blind and quite helpless. But in members of the pheasant family—such as roul-rouls (overleaf)—nests are generally built on or close to the ground and chicks can forage for themselves within a few hours of hatching.

Calyptomena viridis Green broadbill **Burung takau**

Even the most brightly coloured birds can be difficult to see in the shadowy interior of the rain forest. A green broadbill (opposite) among the foliage can be all but invisible. This bird is often the first to call at dawn. Calls are clearly a valuable aid to locating birds. So, too, is the discovery of a favoured feeding-ground: in a fruiting tree may be found the fairy bluebird (right) as well as barbets, bulbuls, pigeons, leafbirds, and hornbills; in a flowering tree there may be sunbirds, flowerpeckers, white-eyes, spiderhunters, and hanging parrots.

In many species of birds the males have showy plumage whereas the females, to be well concealed on the nest, are dowdy. This is true of the ground-dwelling roul-rouls (below) and others of the pheasant family. Birds of this family may be fairly common in undisturbed forest but they are shy and rarely seen.

Irena puella Fairy bluebird **Murai gajah**

Rollulus roulroul Crested wood-partridge/Roul-roul **Burung siul**

Callosciurus caniceps Grey-bellied squirrel **Tupai teratak**/*Musa acuminata* A wild banana GS

The mammals are characterised by the presence of hair, and of mammary glands for feeding the young on milk. Like the birds, mammals arose from reptilian ancestors. Rodents were among the early mammals, first appearing some 50 million years ago; they are now the most numerous and widespread of all mammal groups, and in South-East Asia are exceeded in numbers of species only by the bats.

Callosciurus notatus Red-bellied or plantain squirrel **Tupai pinang**

Rats, porcupines, and the flying squirrels (all rodents) are nocturnal animals and not often seen. But the non-flying squirrels are the mammals of the rain forest most readily observed by day. The grey-bellied squirrel (opposite) is found from Peninsular Malaysia northwards and is especially common in secondary growth and cultivated areas. The plantain squirrel (above) is found throughout South-East Asia south of Thailand, in the lower canopy levels of lowland and hill forest as well as in plantations and gardens. The diet of squirrels is mainly fruit and insects.

Hylobates lar White-handed gibbon **Ungka tangan putih**

Hylobates syndactylus Siamang **Siamang** C

Pongo pygmaeus Orang-utan **Mawas** C

In almost any little-disturbed area of rain forest in South-East Asia, a characteristic sound of the early morning is the calling of gibbons. The white-handed gibbon (main picture) favours the lowlands while the siamang (upper left) is more common in hill forest. Neither of these species occurs in Borneo, but there are other gibbon species, equally vociferous, present there.

Never known on the Malay Peninsula but still surviving precariously in Sumatra and Borneo, is the orang-utan (lower left, with hours-old infant). All three animals pictured are members of the ape family, generally considered, in terms of intelligence, to be the most advanced of all mammal groups.

Apes have no tail, and move by swinging beneath the branches (brachiating), whereas their close relatives the monkeys (as on p. 12) usually have a tail, and walk or run along the branch tops using all four limbs. Apes and monkeys are active by day, but are wary and difficult to approach closely in the rain forest.

Tapirus indicus Tapir **Cipan/Tenuk/Badak murai**

Two major groups within the mammals are the hoofed animals and the carnivores. Rain-forest representatives of the latter group include the otter (pp. 10—11), the civet cat (p. 157), the bear, and the true cats. The hoofed animals are divided into the odd-toed, such as the tapir and rhinoceros, and the even-toed, such as deer, pig, gaur, and serow. Almost all these animals are nocturnal—the otter being an exception—and even those which are relatively common are rarely seen.

The tapir, black with a white "saddle", rests in a thicket by day, its colour pattern breaking up its outline. Its calf (left) is even better camouflaged, and only assumes the adult markings after about three months. The tapir feeds on leaves of the forest undergrowth. It is present in lowland and hill forest in Sumatra and the Malay Peninsula. Tapirs became extinct in Borneo about 9,000 years ago.

Sus scrofa Wild pig **Babi hutan**

Two of the hoofed mammals which may be seen in daylight are the wild pig and the barking deer. The natural distribution of the wild pig extends from western Europe to Japan and Java, but in Borneo its place is taken by the bearded pig, *Sus barbatus*. Pigs are common animals of the rain forest and adjoining areas of cultivation. They create extensive boggy patches alongside streams where groups of animals churn up the soil in search of edible roots. The mature boar (above) bears conspicuous tusks in the lower jaw, and leads a mostly solitary life.

Muntiacus muntjak Barking deer **Kijang**

The barking deer rests by day but is on the move before dusk, browsing on the leaves of seedlings or herbs, or perhaps emerging from cover to feed at a salt-lick. The call is an abrupt gruff roar. The male, in season, bears short two-tined antlers. Barking deer are exceptionally alert and keen-sensed animals—a fact not unrelated to their status as the principal prey (along with the pig) of the tiger.

(*Helarctos malayanus* Malayan sun bear **Beruang**)

(*Capricornis sumatraensis* Serow **Kambing gurun**)

(*Elephas maximus* Indian elephant **Gajah**)

(*Cervus unicolor* Sambar deer **Rusa**)

For most visitors to the rain forest, sightings of large mammals are unlikely unless the facilities of an observation hide are available (see p. 154). There may be some small consolation, however, in the finding and identification of droppings or tracks. Those of the elephant can hardly be mistaken. But droppings of the bear may be confused with those of some fruit-eating civet cats. Those of the serow (a relative of cattle and goats) are most likely to be found on limestone ledges—an unlikely habitat for the sambar deer which produces similar pellets.

(*Panthera tigris* Tiger **Harimau belang**)

(*Bos gaurus* Gaur **Seladang**)

(*Cervus unicolor* Sambar deer **Rusa**)

(*Tapirus indicus* Tapir **Cipan/Tenuk/Badak murai**)

The gaur's track is much larger than the sambar deer's, which in turn is usually distinct from the pig's since in soft ground the pig's shows four toes, the upper pair as well as the lower. Tracks of the rare Sumatran rhinoceros are usually 18 centimetres or more across, while the tapir's (also showing three toes—although it has a fourth, high on the front foot) are 17 centimetres or less. Adult tiger tracks in general are not less than 10 centimetres across while those of a leopard or panther are usually about 8 centimetres. A barefoot human may leave a somewhat similar imprint, but cat tracks show only four pads. Claw marks are visible in tracks of the bear, the wild dog, and civets.

The Functioning of the Forest

Ecology is the study of the relationships between living things and their natural environment. A study of the ecology of a species of hawk moth, for instance, might reveal that the larvae feed on the leaves of two or three particular kinds of trees, that they are subject to predation by certain wasps which lay their eggs within the larva's body, and that the adult moths assist in the pollination of certain species of night-flowering plants and fall prey to insectivorous bats and nightjars. Ecology, then, is the establishment of linkages. Innumerable linkages together form the web which enables the functioning of the forest as a whole. The linkages are not rigid, but allow room for some variation without threat to the overall system.

In matters of technology, it is generally accepted that the more complex a system is—that is the more linkages it involves—the greater is the chance it will break down. But in nature, the more complex the system, the greater is the chance it will successfully resist destabilising forces. The secret of the stability of the rain-forest ecosystem lies in its very complexity and diversity.

Every potential food source in the rain forest is, in chemical or physical terms, unique. Most plants employ some form of protection to enhance their chance of survival. Many contain toxins in their tissues; different plants have different toxins. Where a particular animal or parasitic plant develops a tolerance to the toxins in one plant, this will very likely not be effective against those in another plant. In terms of physical attributes, seeds may be especially hard, bark and fruits may contain sticky resin, stems may be spiny, tubers may contain irritant crystals, flowers may have narrow or deep entrances. Such defences succeed in discouraging most threats, but rarely if ever all.

Animals, too, employ protective strategies: the distastefulness of some butterflies to birds; the spiny defence of the porcupine; the nesting bird's camouflage; the bee's sting; the acute senses and swift flight of the barking deer; the communal protection of the gaur herd. But again none is without a predator that can somewhere find a weakness, at some stage of the life cycle.

Even if, over a long period, some plant or animal evolves better defences or the capacity to utilise a wider range of food sources, these must evolve within the system. During this same period, other components of the system will evolve to take advantage of any new development or to pioneer new defences to counter it. The web retains its stability.

The consequence of all this is that a chance proliferation of a single species (such as a fungus or a locust which might destroy vast tracts of a crop like wheat) can only affect a tiny section of the rain-forest web. And because it is a closed system, the forest will already contain predators that will benefit from such a proliferation, and so help to contain it. The rain-forest system, like a sentient being, exerts its own discipline.

Chance does seem to play a part as well as design. The reason that every tree in the forest does not succumb to the strangling fig is presumably because there is no more than a slim probability that the fig's seed can be deposited in a suitable place and prosper there. Chance ensures that some members of any prey species will escape predation long enough to breed, and some of any plant species, whatever the onslaught, will survive to reproduce their kind. Failure brings about the rare event, under natural circumstances, of extinction.

If only it were left to itself, the overwhelming probability is that the tropical rain-forest ecosystem would, in the future, continue to exist much as it has done for millennia past.

Ficus sp., a strangling fig, and *Koompassia excelsa,* **Tualang**

No other natural environments in the world offer such perfect conditions for plant growth as do the moist tropical lowlands. Adequate nutrients are available (though only in the top few centimetres of the soil); there is abundant rainfall; there is a wealth of energy from sunlight, rarely a day passing without at least one or two hours of sunshine; and temperatures are uniformly high year-round.

Competition among plants, especially for light, is intense. Different plants adapt in different ways so that no growth opportunity is wasted. Of plants that germinate on the forest floor, some stay small, thriving only in shady conditions, while others develop tall columnar trunks so that their leaves can be exposed to direct sunlight. The strangling fig (opposite) may ultimately conquer forest giants, though its seedling is unable to survive in the dimness of the forest floor; it can only germinate successfully high up on a branch where the light is brighter (see pp. 42–3).

In most parts of tropical South-East Asia, annual rainfall exceeds 2,000 millimetres, and rain falls on about 150 days of the year. In few places are there more than two months of the year where rainfall is less than 60 millimetres per month, and in monsoonal areas the wettest months may produce 600 millimetres. Rain throughout the year ensures a near-constant growing season. Growth may be checked, however, due to moisture stress during drier periods. The onset of such periods is believed to induce deciduousness in some dominant species, and for many kinds of forest trees the resumption of regular rains is an inducement to flowering.

Mangifera foetida Wild mango **Macang**

Rain-forest seedlings suffer fierce root competition from other plants, and a very large proportion die in the first year after germination. Moist fleshy fruits like those of the mango (left) may be less dependent on rainfall for the first stages of germination and growth, but production of the dry fruits of dipterocarp trees (see p. 74, left) is usually timed to coincide with a wet period when the ground will be damp. Although mature dipterocarps are among the most light-demanding trees of the lowland rain forest, their seedlings are able to germinate in great abundance (below) in the very low light conditions of the forest floor.

Beyond the first year, the surviving seedlings of most light-demanding tree species will stagnate and die unless a gap is created in the forest canopy overhead by the death of a large tree (opposite). Only then, with available light greatly increased, can the strongest young trees shoot up and prosper. But in shade-tolerant, non-dominant tree species such as the mango, saplings can grow tall without the need for large gaps, so long as there is space for growth among existing vegetation.

Shorea maxwelliana **Balau kumus hitam** STS

Aporusa sp.

Eugenia sp.

Saraca sp.

Dipterocarpus sp.

◀ In the tropical rain forest, a feature of the development of new leaves—both in mature trees and in seedlings—is the tendency towards bright colours. Red, orange, pink, mauve, and even blue leaves may be encountered, though how such coloration might advantageously serve the plant is unclear. It is also common for new leaves, and often their stems as well, to hang soft and limp. Only when the leaves have grown to full size do the tissues thicken and stiffen, and develop their mature-green colour.

Most rain-forest trees lose their old leaves and develop new ones progressively through the year, and thus overall the forest appears evergreen. But in many tree species the production of new leaves (right) is concentrated into a short—and often colourful—season. The effect is particularly striking (below) where there is a season of markedly drier weather—as in southern Thailand during December/January, and during February/March in rain-shadow areas of central Pahang, Peninsular Malaysia. Here the lowland forest contains some deciduous tree species which lose all their old leaves and stand bare for days or weeks (see pp. 4–5 and 72–3) until the new leaves sprout, usually with the return of rainy weather.

N.I. BL

STP

Christisonia scortechinii GS

Some plants of the rain forest can function altogether without leaves. Parasitic flowering plants such as *Christisonia* (opposite) and *Epirixanthes* (right) do not manufacture their own materials for growth, but tap the roots of other plants. *Christisonia* is specifically a parasite of bamboo. Certain species of *Burmannia* (far right) function similarly but draw upon dead and decaying material rather than on a living host, and are termed saprophytes. (Most species of fungi—pp. 54–7—are saprophytic, the rest parasitic.)

Dendrophthoe, a species of mistletoe, is termed a hemi-parasite. Its sticky seed, perhaps wiped from a bird's beak, germinates on the damp bark of a tree branch; specialised root-like structures (haustoria) then penetrate the stem of the host plant to draw on the sap flow. But to augment this food supply the plant produces its own leaves which function in the usual way.

▼

Epirixanthes cylindrica

Burmannia championii PL

Dendrophthoe pentandra A mistletoe GS

While some plants are dependent upon others for their survival, most notably it is the animals that depend on plants, directly or indirectly. The benefit, however is far from one-sided. While animals may be widely destructive to plants on which they feed, they may also be constructive. The cave fruit bat feeds on soft fruits and nectar; it is believed to play a vital role in the pollination of the nocturnal flowers of the **durian**, so initiating development of the commercially valuable fruit and the production of seeds.

Eonycteris spelaea Cave fruit bat **Cecadu gua**

Durio zibethinus Durian **Durian** GS

By day, flies and beetles (right) and bees (below) visit flowers to obtain food—as do butterflies, nectar-feeding birds, and even squirrels (p. 106). In so doing they all inadvertently transfer pollen from anther to stigma, either within the flower visited (self-fertilisation) or between flowers (cross-fertilisation). In many instances of plant-animal interaction it is clear that there is considerable structural adaptation on the part of plant or animal, or both, to ensure some benefit for each partner.

Lithocarpus ?gracilis **Mempening**

Xylocopa latipes Carpenter bee **Kumbang**/*Dillenia ovata* **Simpuh beludu**

Parameria polyneura PT

Chloropsis cyanopogon Lesser green leafbird **Burung daun**/*Ficus benjamina* **Beringin**

In the largest trees of the lowland rain forest, and in climbers and epiphytes of the upper canopy, wind is generally the agent of pollination, and subsequently of seed distribution. Wind-distributed seeds are generally of the parachute type (above left), or bear wings of some kind (as in *Dipterocarpus*, p .74, left), or are so tiny as to be almost like dust, as in the seeds of orchids and the spores of ferns and fungi. Plants of the lower strata of the forest tend to have fruits attractive to animals. These will either be consumed on the tree (by birds, monkeys, squirrels, flying foxes …), or fall to the ground and be eaten there (by civet cats, deer, bears …). Hard seeds pass through the digestive system and are deposited, often far from the parent tree, in the animals' droppings. A single fig tree in heavy fruit (left) can attract more than fifty different species of birds—a situation of great benefit to the fig, to the birds, and to bird-watchers!

130

No rain-forest plant functions wholly independently of animal life, for ultimately all plants rely on the efficient recycling of nutrients. Termites (right) have the capacity to break down cellulose—a major constituent of all plant matter—through the presence of special protozoa in their digestive tracts. Most species of termites feed entirely on dead plant material, from tree trunks to twigs and dry leaves. Many, including *Macrotermes*, build large well-ventilated nests in the soil (p. 91), and much of the food material is borne back to the nest a tiny morsel at a time. Thus the termites play a major role in both the enrichment and aeration of the forest soil. Various beetles and their larvae also help to break down dead wood, as do free-living bacteria.

The other major agents of decay and recycling are the fungi. Some species do attack living plants, but a great many fungi grow in dead wood, as evidenced by the fruiting bodies so commonly seen sprouting from fallen trunks and branches.

Macrotermes carbonarius A termite **Anai-anai**

Cookeina sulcipes (Sarcoscyphaceae) A cup fungus

Atrophaneura varuna GS

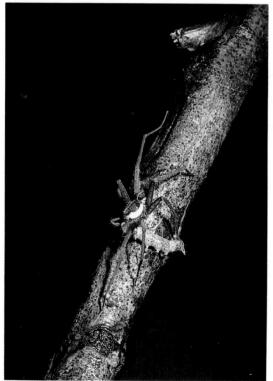

N.I.

Rana chalconota Copper-cheeked frog **Katak tembaga**

No rain-forest animal functions wholly independently of the forest itself, since every chain of predator-prey relationships leads back to direct dependence on plant food. The owl eats the snake eats the frog eats the spider eats the caterpillar eats the leaf. Every plant and every animal in the rain forest, indigenous hunting-and-gathering humans included, fits into the overall web, each linked to and dependent upon other members of the community. Populations of any given species may wax and wane but the web always adjusts to accommodate. All is in delicate equilibrium.

Bubo sumatranus Barred eagle owl **Burung hantu bubu**

Dendrelaphis sp. A bronze-back tree snake

The Forest by Night

Total darkness, such that even after many minutes of adjustment the eyes still cannot discern tree from leaf or path from blackness; odd rustlings now and then, perhaps just a leaf falling, or perhaps the calculated movement of something larger; an odour, rank, wafting by and then gone; tiny lights, pale green, bobbing along noiselessly through the undergrowth; above the constant buzz and ring of insects, an eerie call, close by, repeated again and again; a puff of wind on the cheek and the muffled flutter of fast-beating wings; momentarily a soft infusion of blue-white light, flashing, from a distant storm; and thunder. The sheer mystery and potency of the unseen and unknown can hardly be greater anywhere than on a moonless night in virgin lowland tropical rain forest. Yet for the rain-forest wildlife-watcher, there is no better place and time.

On a night walk by torchlight, observation is concentrated within the narrow pool of light from the torch beam. By day small animals such as insects tend to be overlooked amid the complexity of the whole forest vista, but at night they can be more easily picked out from their surroundings. Although few birds can be found after dark, in general there is a greater variety of wildlife to be seen at night than by day. In the mammals there are far more nocturnal than diurnal species; and the mammals of the night are far easier to spot.

Nocturnal animals have a reflector at the back of the eye, which intensifies the image registered, and also returns a fiery glow when struck by the light of a torch. The effect is particularly strong in mammals, but is also found in owls and their kin, geckos, frogs, and even moths and spiders. If the torch is held close by the observer's head, then the "eye-shine" reflection is seen at its brightest. With stealth it may be possible to draw close to shy animals since they are dazzled by the light and must rely on other senses.

Activity for most nocturnal animals begins just before dusk. Flying squirrels might, with luck, be observed working their way up to the highest branch of a tall tree, and launching themselves to glide majestically out of sight. Bats stream out of caves. Civet cats emerge from day-time hiding places.

The switch to the night shift is marked by a sometimes quite extraordinarily rich concert performance, with contributions from the retiring day-workers as well as those waking up for the night. Monkeys, hornbills, cicadas, frogs, nightjars, and crickets are just a few of the players. But after an hour or so the excitement is over, until at dawn the sound level peaks again, with quite different contributors, mainly birds, and perhaps gibbons.

No rain forest journey can be judged complete without an experience of the forest by night. The richest rewards will be gained from an overnight sojourn, camped in the forest, or in an observation hide, if available. On a pitch-black night the fireflies and the phosphorescent fungi are startling in their brightness. By the full moon the forest is enchanting. There is no cause for fear in the forest at night; but there is ample cause for awe.

Oroxylum indicum Midnight horror **Bonglai**

Barringtonia fusiformis **Putat**

Barringtonia fusiformis **Putat**

Animal life observed by night in the rain forest may be altogether different from that encountered by day; but the forest vegetation, whatever the hour, shows little apparent change. A few rain-forest plants do, however, take special advantage of nocturnal animal life. Flowers of *Barringtonia* (opposite) burst from their buds at dusk. During the night some will be successfully pollinated by small nectar-feeding moths, or perhaps by bats. By dawn the flower heads have fallen (above), to form a carpet beneath the tree. The buds at the bottom of the inflorescence open first, and on each subsequent night several more buds will open progressively higher up the stem until all have flowered. The female part of the flower is left behind, whether or not fertilisation has taken place.

The massive pods of the **bonglai** tree (previous page) develop from large foul-smelling flowers which open at dusk and fall before dawn. Nectar-feeding bats are attracted by the odour and pollinate the flowers as they feed. Their tell-tale claw-marks are evident in the fleshy petals of fallen blooms (right).

Oroxylum indicum Midnight horror **Bonglai**

138

On a night walk it is the noisy animals and the large-eyed animals which are most likely to be caught in the torch's beam. But with concentration focused within the spotlight, small and unobtrusive nocturnal animals can also be located. Snails are out at night in search of their vegetable diet, feelers probing the way before them. Their shell is their haven during the day. Some snails (below) have an extra disc of shell (the operculum) attached to the body; when the snail is completely withdrawn this seals off the entrance of the shell proper.

Amphidromus sp.

Cyclophorus aquilus GS

Scolopendra sp. **Lipan**

By night the centipede emerges from day-time hiding to hunt its prey—mainly insects. The red *Scolopendra* grows to more than 20 centimetres in length and can inflict a painful poisonous bite if carelessly handled. The scorpion (see p.88) also hunts by night, either lying in wait at the entrance of a burrow, or roaming at large.

Gymnogryllus brachyxiphus A ground cricket **Keridik** GS

Tympanophyllum arcufolium A long-horned grasshopper

Many nocturnal animals can be located by the sounds they make as they call to attract a mate or to register territorial claims. Male crickets are major contributors to the rain forest's night-time noise, vibrating their wing-bases to produce the sounds. A ground-dwelling species, *Gymnogryllus* (left), at nightfall prepares at its burrow entrance a "singing ground". This is concave-shaped to reflect and substantially amplify the cricket's call. At the slightest ground vibration the cricket will instantly disappear inside.

Related to the crickets are the long-horned grasshoppers (or katydids). That pictured (right) makes a short deep humming sound (mooorp! ... mooorp! ...) which carries a great distance. But locating the well-camouflaged source is quite a challenge!

Rana glandulosa Glandular frog **Katak kelenjar**

Otus bakkamoena Collared scops owl **Burung hantu reban**

Owls and frogs also add to the night noise. The hand-sized scops owls (above) have a short, soft, penetrating whistle. Pinpointing the source of the call in the spotlight is aided by the strongly reflective capacity of the owl's large eyes. Owls generally perch on a low branch, waiting for the sound or sight of prey on which to swoop.

Frogs can be especially vociferous and are quite easily found along any stream in the forest, either through their calling or by eye-shine. Usually it is only the males that call. The light will not distract them, and with luck their throat-ballooning concert can be enjoyed from very close quarters.

Rana blythi Malayan giant frog **Katak demam**

Polypedates colletti Hour-glass bush frog **Katak pokok potongan**

Rana miopus Three-striped frog **Katak tiga garis**

Rana hosei Green tree frog **Katak pokok hijau**

Microhyla berdmorei Hour-glass froglet **Katak belalang**

Rana blythi (opposite) is among the largest of the South-East Asian frogs and may grow to a handspan in length. Many smaller frogs are brightly coloured or attractively patterned, but none is poisonous (as are some in South America). Rain-forest frogs may be found far from streams as well as near them, and high in the trees as well as on the ground.

N.I. A huntsman spider

N.I. A huntsman spider

N.I.

N.I. A huntsman spider

Most spiders have eight eyes in a tight cluster on the top of the head. By night in the beam of a torchlight these reflect brightly like the sparkle of a tiny diamond. Jumping spiders are active by day, but most spiders are mainly active at night. It is then that the huntsman spiders of the Sparassidae family (left) emerge from hiding. They do not build webs to trap prey, but lie in wait and pounce upon whatever edible passes their way. The same applies to the hairy mygalomorph (below and opposite). This spider, big enough to fill a tea-cup, makes its home in a tree-hole or burrow and feeds on large insects, frogs, and perhaps even small birds. (One in captivity lived for five and a half years on diet of young white mice.) Its offspring may number more than 150 per brood. All spiders have a poisonous bite, but none in South-East Asia is dangerous to humans. The bite of the mygalomorph is said to be no worse than a bee's sting.

Phormingochilus sp. A hairy mygalomorph

Phormingochilus sp. A hairy mygalomorph

Tragulus javanicus

Tragulus javanicus Lesser mousedeer **Pelanduk**

For most people exploring the rain forest by night, it is the eye-shine of mammalian wildlife which really sets the pulse racing—perhaps because with mammals in the undergrowth it is difficult to judge whether two large eyes are those of a small animal very near, or a large animal farther away!

The lesser mousedeer ranks with the world's smallest hoofed animals, and is no bigger than a domestic cat. (Another species, the greater mousedeer or **napoh**, is slightly larger, but otherwise very similar in appearance and habits.) Mousedeer may be active by day or night. They are exceedingly shy and rarely seen by day, but at night with a strong light they can be closely approached. They feed on leaves and fruits.

The slow loris, unlike its relatives the monkeys and apes, never leaps from tree to tree, but moves methodically along the branches hand over hand. It is one of very few nocturnal primates (the tarsier of Borneo is another) and one of the few which are carnivorous. The loris feeds on insects and on small vertebrates such as frogs, pouncing upon them suddenly and swiftly after a stealthy approach.

Nycticebus coucang Slow loris **Kongkang** GS

Cyriopalus wallacei A longicorn beetle GS

Many night-flying insects of the rain forest such as moths, cicadas, flying termites, and some beetles are, for reasons still not fully understood, attracted to light. Scientists set up special light-traps to collect such insects, and quite different species are found up in the forest canopy and down in the understorey. Longicorn beetles (as above, retrieved from a low-level moth trap) develop from wood-boring larvae. The larva pupates within the wood, and the adult emerges from the tree to fly off and mate. Eggs are laid in a bark crevice.

Cockchafer beetles, when not flying at light bulbs, may be major pests of some tropical crops. Their eggs are laid in the soil. The larvae feed on plant roots, and in many species pupate underground.

Lepidiota stigma A cockchafer beetle GS

Diaphanes sp. A firefly **Kelip-kelip** GS

A much smaller beetle—generally only about a centimetre long— is the firefly (above), which generates its own light by a remarkable process of organic chemistry in a special organ in its abdomen. Individual fireflies flashing intermittently in flight are quite a common sight in the rain forest at night. These are males. The females of most species are wingless, but they too display phosphorescence, as do the larvae; both can readily be found on or close to the ground. Fireflies are at least partly predatory on other insects, and the light they emit may help to attract prey. It also plays a part in the attraction of a mate.

Small phosphorescent toadstools may locally be abundant ▶ among the lowland forest undergrowth, a cluster producing a light bright enough for the reading of a printed page. Fallen leaves commonly become impregnated with phosphorescent fungal threads, so that on a pitch-dark night, and allowing time for the eyes to adjust, the whole forest floor may be seen to glow eerily. The property of phosphorescence in toadstools has been claimed to attract night-flying insects to the fungus, so aiding in distribution of spores.

Mycena sp. (Tricholomataceae)

Walking by night in the rain forest affords little chance of observing large mammals, their population density being sparse compared with that of, for instance, rats or mousedeer. Most large mammals are nocturnally active, however, and many of the herbivores supplement their diet with added minerals obtained from naturally salt-rich sites in the forest. At such "salt-licks" there is usually a spring, where minerals may crystallise in powdery deposits (below left). Hides such as that in Taman Negara, Peninsular Malaysia (left), permit discreet observation of the salt-lick area.

Salt-licks are focus-points for wildlife such as the tapir, elephant, gaur (below right), barking deer, and sambar deer (opposite). Gaur, a form of wild cattle found from the Malay Peninsula northwards to India, move in herds of as many as twenty animals, presided over by a dominant bull. The species is seriously endangered. Sambar deer are more common, though widely hunted. The stag develops impressive antlers which are shed after the breeding season each year. The doe produces a single fawn.

Large animals can usually be heard as they approach a salt-lick. They are generally unperturbed by strong lights held steadily on them, and often remain in view for many minutes.

Bos gaurus Gaur **Seladang**

Cervus unicolor Sambar deer **Rusa**

Cervus unicolor Sambar deer **Rusa**

156

Gekko smithi

The hide itself (or any other building in the rain forest) may prove attractive to wildlife. The giant gecko (above) normally resides by day in a hole in a tree, but will readily adapt to life in a secluded corner of a building, coming out of hiding by night to hunt for insects. The flying gecko (right) has flaps of skin along the flanks, legs, and tail, which when fully stretched enable the gecko to glide—or at worst to fall more gently. This species, like the former, is normally a tree-dweller, but may also be found around forest buildings.

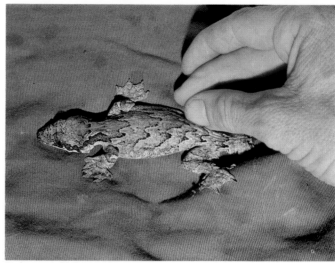

Ptychozoon kuhli Flying gecko

At night, food scraps may attract rats into any forest dwelling. But unlike urban rats, these are clean, sleek-furred animals. There are more than 20 species native to the South-East Asian rain forest. Regularly fed, some will quickly grow tame enough to eat from the hand.

Rubbish left outside may attract a larger visitor, the Malay civet (below). This is one of the largest of the civet cats. It is a carnivorous feeder and does not climb. There are several civet species in the rain forest, and all, like the rats, are nocturnal.

Rats and civets, according to species, may be wholly arboreal, or spend some or all of their time on the ground. Some are primarily predators, some favour a mixed diet, and the rest feed on vegetable matter such as fruits.

Rattus exulans Burmese rat **Tikus rumah kecil** GS

Viverra tangalunga Malay civet **Tenggalung**

LIMESTONE HI

Gua Peningat, Pahang, Peninsular Malaysia

LS AND CAVES

ANY traveller in the lowlands of Sumatra, the Malay Peninsula, or Borneo, will almost certainly encounter massive monoliths of limestone rock, here and there poking abruptly out of an otherwise flat or undulating landscape.

In their shape the limestone outcrops often appear like a tooth, a large molar of the lower jaw, almost vertical-sided but with an irregular somewhat dome-shaped top. The distance across these outcrops may be from less than a hundred metres to more than a kilometre. They may be eroded down to a level close to that of the surrounding country or they may stand several hundred metres high. Gunung Api in Sarawak is entirely limestone and almost 1,800 metres high.

Many limestone outcrops are still surrounded by rain forest. In contrast with this vegetation is that on the limestone itself—taking root in the meagre soil across the top of the outcrop and in such crevices as are available up the steep flanks. The plants of this specialised environment are generally quite different from those of the surrounding forest. The wildlife may be different too. Many species of snails are found only associated with limestone; whistling thrushes (*Myiophoneus*) may be common there, nesting on rock ledges and feeding on snails; and in Sumatra and the Malay Peninsula the serow (a wild goat) favours steep country, often the limestone outcrops.

The formation of the outcrops, and of the caves so often present within them, arose through a complex process of sedimentation, uplift, and erosion. The limestone was originally laid down beneath the sea, built up as layers of lime mud originating in corals, shells, and other calcareous materials. Ultimately this was compressed into rock, uplifted, and folded, becoming part of the land mass.

Limestone rock will very slowly dissolve in slightly acid water. Thus, in a limestone landscape, with the passage of millions of years "sink holes" develop. These are apertures down which naturally acidic surface water runs to form underground streams and caves. Eventually much of the land is undermined and collapses, leaving cliff-faced outcrops standing in a surrounding area of limestone bedrock (often overlain by alluvial sediments) or of older sedimentary rocks.

The caves within these remnant outcrops can be of immense size and spectacular structure. Stalactites and stalagmites do occur, but in beauty and complexity they rarely match those found in caves of temperate climates. The wildlife in these tropical caves may, however, be far richer than that in caves elsewhere. Bats, often in tens of thousands, are primary colonisers. In turn many other forms of animal life depend directly or indirectly on the bats. Swiftlets (*Callocalia*) may also be primary colonisers.

All cave life ultimately depends on the forest, for it is here that the bats and swiftlets feed. In so doing they keep insect populations in check, and those bats feeding on nectar and fruit serve to pollinate some flowers and distribute seeds. The limestone hills and caves, wherever present, are an integral part of the surrounding rain-forest ecosystem.

The most extensive cave system yet discovered in South-East Asia is that in the Mulu National Park, Sarawak. It is known to only a few experienced spelaeologists. The Niah caves, also part of Sarawak's National Park system, are accessible to visitors, and are the focus of important archaeological work by the Sarawak Museum. Here also there is commercial collection of guano and of the edible nests of swiftlets. Most photographs in this chapter were taken in Taman Negara, Peninsular Malaysia, where two caves rich in animal life—Gua Telinga and Gua Daun Menari—are easily accessible, yet little disturbed.

Many caves elsewhere invite exploration. Some may feel that walking—or crawling—through malodorous spongy-soft guano is less than ideal recreation. But there is little to fear, least of all the bats, and much to fascinate. All that is needed is an adventurous spirit, reliable torches, sound common sense, and a hole in the side of a limestone hill.

TLB

BBL

Pandanus irregularis BBL

Impatiens mirabilis Gouty balsam TLB

Calanthe ceciliae GC

Limestone outcrops can be explored in three ways: around them, over them, and inside them. Around them there are fine views, with the lowland forest giving way to lofty walls of rock; over them there is the challenge of the ascent, foothold and handhold and perhaps (top left) a little tree-climbing; and inside them there is all the mystery and excitement of dark, damp caves, often rich in wildlife.

For those prepared to climb, besides views from high vantage points there is the attraction of the unusual vegetation on the limestone. The rock and its crevices offer plants the exposed habitats typical of the mountains, but with the high temperatures and rainless periods characteristic of the lowlands. Some plants—like the **kerjim** palm (opposite) with its curtain of aerial roots—may thrive in a limestone habitat, but occur in the surrounding rain forest as well. Others, like *Pandanus irregularis*, the balsam *Impatiens mirabilis*, and the orchid *Calanthe ceciliae*, are specialised plants growing almost exclusively on limestone.

Arenga westerhoutii **Kerjim** GC

The **lengkap** palm, formerly named *Arenga westerhoutii,* is now called *Arenga obtusifolia,* and the **kerjim** palm, previously unnamed, is now designated *A. westerhoutii*

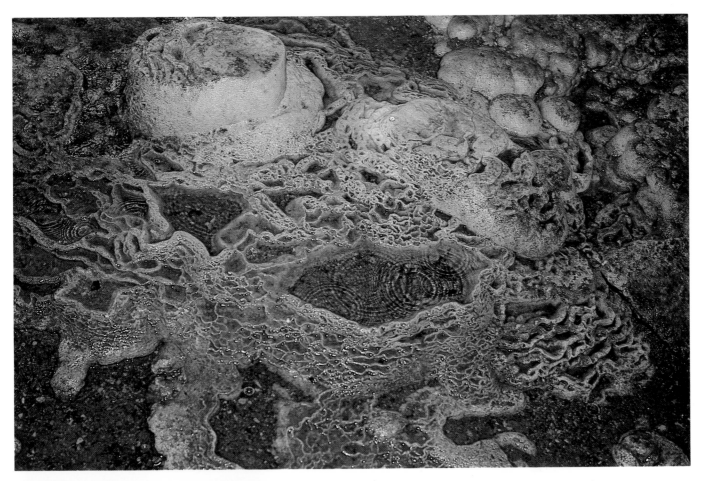

The caves within the limestone outcrops are now mostly above ground level; but they were formed more than 100 million years ago when the surrounding land was much higher. Subterranean streams carved passages through the rock. Lakes formed, dissolving the limestone walls and creating large caverns. As the land eroded the caves were drained of water, and today are dry but for seepage through the roof and down the walls. Stalactites and stalagmites develop, and may unite to form huge pillars (opposite). But whereas in a temperate climate a lower rainfall and lower humidity allows a slow process of recrystallisation of limestone from solution, the moist tropical climate almost always sends another droplet trickling down the cave wall before the last one has evaporated and crystallised. The formations in most South-East Asian caves are therefore largely composed of sediments, only lightly cemented together by crystallisation. The fine structure of many intricately sculptured surfaces (above and left) can be scratched away with a fingernail.

Cave grandeur: a marriage of landscape and architecture, canyon and cathedral.

GC

GC

GC

GC

Above and below: *Hipposideros larvatus* GTL

Colonies of insect-eating bats may number many thousands of individuals. These rest by day packed tightly across the cave ceiling. Bats are the only mammals that can truly fly; and insect bats, together with a few species of shrews, are the only land mammals to use echo-location rather than sight for orientation. Insect bats emit ultrasonic signals from the nostrils; the noseleaves present in horseshoe bats (left and overleaf) and members of some other insect-bat families serve to direct out-going signals, while the complex structure of the ear serves to receive reflected signals.

At dusk the bats emerge from the cave to spend the night hours feeding on insects captured in flight. The undigested remains are deposited on the cave floor next day as guano.

The female horseshoe bat has two sets of nipples, a lactating pair on the chest and a dummy pair in the groin. On this latter pair the baby bat suspends itself by its mouth—head upwards—except while feeding. After four or five weeks the young bat is weaned and leaves the mother to suspend itself by its feet—head downwards—on the cave ceiling.

Hipposideros larvatus Large roundleaf horseshoe bat **Kelawar ladam bulat besar** GTL

Rhinolophus luctus morio Woolly horseshoe bat **Kelawar ladam terbesar** GS

In Peninsular Malaysia alone there are some 75 species of bats, and almost certainly more species still to be discovered. Most, like the horseshoe bats (opposite, and previous page), are insectivorous, but 15 or so are fruit bats (below and right).

Fruit bats tend to be larger; most have a second claw on the wing; and since they do not rely on echo-location their eyes are highly developed and their heads without the often grotesque adornment seen in insect bats. The biggest of the fruit bats, the flying fox with a wing span of 1.5 metres, may sometimes be seen in large flocks flying by day; this species roosts in trees. More typical is the dusky fruit bat, roosting in caves, usually in those parts where some light penetrates. Fruit bats feed on the nectar of flowers and on soft fruits.

Both pictures: *Penthetor lucasi* Dusky fruit bat **Cecadu hitam pudar** GTL

N.I. BBL

Many other kinds of animals live in caves, though all are ultimately dependent on the bats (or, in many Bornean caves, bats and swiftlets). Much of the cave floor is covered with a thick layer of guano in which countless tiny creatures live and feed. Cockroaches (left) burrow in the guano, feeding mainly on dead animal material.

The cave racer snake feeds on live animals, mainly bats which it snatches from the walls or picks up, fallen, from the cave floor. The bat is killed by constriction and then swallowed whole, head first; the entire operation takes only about two minutes. The snake is non-venomous and can grow to a length of more than 1.5 metres.

Elaphe taeniura Cave racer **Ular gua,** and *Hipposideros larvatus* GTL

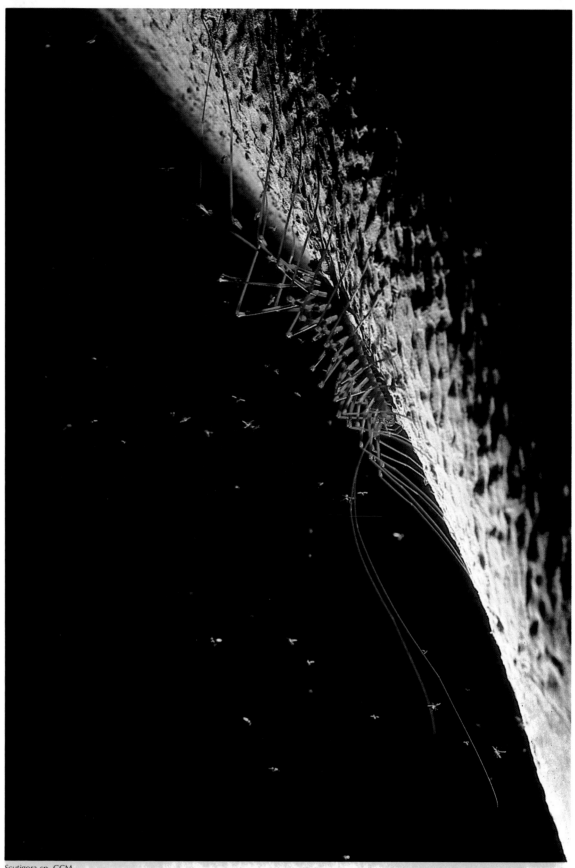

Scutigera sp. GCM

Diestrammena sp. GTL

Among the smaller cave predators is *Scutigera* (opposite), a relative of the centipede. In order to locate its prey in total darkness *Scutigera* has two sets of feelers. At the rear are the immensely long hindmost legs; and on the head are the antennae, borne below the eyes and above the poison fangs. *Scutigera* feeds on insects and other small animal life on the cave walls. Its body grows to about eight centimetres in length.

Diestrammena (above), is a wingless kind of cricket. It is believed to feed on fungus growing on the cave walls and floor. Its long antennae help it to detect the presence of predators—such as *Scutigera*.

The adult cricket is about 2.5 centimetres long. Growth (as in *Scutigera*) is achieved by splitting the old exoskeleton. The layer beneath is initially soft and elastic, allowing room for some enlargement of the body before hardening takes place.

Bufo asper Malayan giant toad **Kodok paru hutan** GTL

Bufo asper is a common cave-dwelling toad, but is also found outside in the forest. It can grow to more than 20 centimetres in length and almost a kilogram in weight. The toad feeds on small animal life. This it catches with its long sticky tongue which, as in frogs, is attached to the front of the mouth and can be shot out and retrieved very rapidly. To detect prey, toads must rely on their large eyes, and in caves they generally inhabit regions where some light penetrates. They are usually solitary.

Among the lower orders of animals, parental care is uncommon. But many kinds of spiders guard their eggs, and the cave-dwelling species (left) carries them with her in a silken sack until they hatch. The amblypygid or whip-spider (below and opposite) goes one step further and holds the eggs in a sort of pouch on the underside of the abdomen. When they hatch the young emerge and cluster on the mother's back.

The amblypygids have a segmented abdomen, and so are classified between the scorpions and the spiders in the animal kingdom. They carry no poison, but capture their prey in their spiny pincers and consume it alive.

Amblypygids have the first pair of legs greatly elongated to serve as feelers. But the spider has little need for special adaptations to cave life; it lives within the confines of its web, and the slender silken strands immediately communicate to the occupant the presence of any entangled prey.

Psechrus ?argentatus GCM

Above and left: *Stygophrynus* sp. A whip spider GTL

MOUNTAI

GUK

N FOREST

THE highest mountains of the Malay Peninsula rise less than 2,200 metres; those along the length of Sumatra are from 2,900 to just over 3,800 metres; and the extraordinary massif of Gunung Kinabalu in Borneo has several peaks over 4,000 metres. The mountains of the Malay Peninsula are mainly granitic in origin (though the highest, Gunung Tahan, is of sedimentary rock). They were formed more than 100 million years ago and have been subject to no more than gentle progressive weathering ever since. Many of the mountains of Sumatra were formed by volcanic action within the last two million years. Some are still active and have erupted during the present century. Kinabalu first appeared only about two million years ago as an upward-thrusting block of solid granitic rock. It is still rising, currently at an estimated seven millimetres a year.

While there is great variety in the origins of the mountains of tropical South-East Asia, there is close similarity in the vegetation that covers them, with many species of plants common to high country in the Malay Peninsula, Borneo, and Sumatra.

In terms of structure and composition there is a distinct type of forest that can be found on almost all high mountains in the region. It is a dwarf forest, less than ten metres tall and in some places only knee-high. Tree trunks lean at all angles, twisted and low-branched, and support a single dense layer of foliage. To limit loss of moisture in the direct sun and near-constant wind, leaves tend to be small, thick, and leathery. Coniferous tree species may be common.

Beneath the canopy of the tree crowns no line can easily be drawn between the habitats of terrestrial and epiphytic plants. The latter grow all the way down to the forest floor, thickly clothing ground, trunks, and branches. Mosses are the most abundant epiphytes, but there are also lichens, ferns, and numerous orchids. Some climbing plants are present, notably rattans and pitcher plants. All is frequently shrouded in mist, and the forest glistens with suspended water droplets.

This, then, is the mountain forest, in character so very far removed from the lowland tropical rain forest. Yet of course the two are connected. The zone between them can conveniently be termed hill forest. It is a transition zone containing progressively fewer huge buttressed trees, and giving way to a forest of more slender, not-so-tall, not-so-straight trees, where more light filters through to the forest floor. Different kinds of plants occur here, such that in the space of a few hours' uphill journey on foot, the species composition of the forest can change almost completely. There will also, very largely, be a different complement of mammals, birds, frogs, insects .... In sounds, too, the hill forest is different from the lowlands: different cicadas, different gibbons calling, different birdsong. It even feels different. Perhaps there is a breeze. Certainly the air is cooler. And in many hill forest areas there are no leeches.

Higher up still, ridge flanks become steeper and the crests narrower. Here the mossy mountain forest first appears; but it may occur at markedly different altitudes on different mountains. In an extensive mountainous region, certain pitcher plants and montane conifers may grow nowhere below 1,500 metres; but on an isolated peak only 600 metres high, wherever there is shallow soil on exposed rocky ridges these same plant species might be found.

What then gives rise to the mountain forest? Lower temperatures and higher rainfall can be no more than contributory factors. Exposure seems to be the main cause of its occurrence: a site open to sun and wind at all hours of the day, and through which mist frequently drifts; and, perhaps most important of all, a site where bedrock occurs at or close to the surface and there is a paucity of mineral soil.

On the harshest sites, over many thousands of years plant life can progressively cushion exposure, encrusting bare rock and building up the beginnings of an organic soil. Ultimately, a forest may grow, having created its own highly specialised living environment. Only on the very highest peaks and around volcanic craters might this uppermost limit of tropical rain forest gain no foothold at all.

Livistona tahanensis **Serdang Tahan** GT

Lithocarpus gracilis **Mempening**

Dipteris conjugata GSB

It may take a day or more to trek from the tall lowland rain forest of the valleys and lesser hills up to the stunted vegetation of the high ridges and peaks (far left). The change, then, is a gradual one.

The **seraya** (p. 75) and, at higher altitudes, the **damar minyak** (p. 67) are characteristic trees of the hill forest of intermediate altitudes in Peninsular Malaysia. The acorn fruits (left) of a few species of the oak family can be found in the lowlands; but in the mountains dipterocarp trees all but disappear from the forest, and throughout the region it is oaks of many species which largely replace them. Where the soil is more shallow and the forest canopy thins and allows more light through, the montane ferns *Dipteris* (below left) and, on especially exposed sites, *Matonia* (below right) may appear. Both tend to establish small colonies since their spreading network of rapid-growing underground stems is able to crowd out less vigorous plants.

Matonia pectinata GBB

In sheltered parts of the hill forest such as gullies and saddles herbs may grow more abundantly than in the lowlands. The differences in habitat are subtle but significant: in the hills there is a change in soil chemistry, higher rainfall and frequent mists, more air movement, more light on the forest floor, and cooler temperatures. Only a tiny proportion of the plant species of the lowland forest at 100 metres altitude is present at 1,000 metres altitude; and the same is true for animal life. The forest herb *Didymocarpus platypus* is one of that tiny proportion, and while it is most commonly found in hill forest, it occurs in some lowland localities as well.

Didymocarpus platypus FH

Dacrydium comosum **Ekor tupai lebat** GUK

GBB

A striking difference in vegetation is evident on exposed mountain ridgetops. Erosion renders the mineral soil thin and nutrient-deficient, but in its place an organic soil is built up from rotting plant material. In this environment tree growth is stunted, with trunks often tortuously twisted and leaning, and branch-tips bent with the prevailing winds. *Dacrydium comosum* (opposite), a coniferous tree with distinctive squirrel-tail foliage, is restricted in range to this ridgetop zone.

In the perpetually damp conditions beneath, many small and attractive plants thrive (above). Mosses not only cover the ground but blanket tree trunks and branches—so visually dominant that it is usual for this montane vegetation to be termed mossy forest.

Some species of mosses—the best-known is *Sphagnum* (right)— can grow where there is virtually no soil. Even on rock they create their own growing environment, building up a deep spongy mat capable of rapidly absorbing large quantities of water whenever it is available. As mineral and organic matter accumulates underneath, other plants tolerant of these conditions can find a foothold. Typical of such exposed montane habitats are the fragrant-leafed *Baeckea frutescens* (below), and *Leptospermum flavescens* (opposite) with its readily recognisable flowers and fruits. Both plants, according to the constraints of their environment, may be anything from knee-high shrubs to small trees.

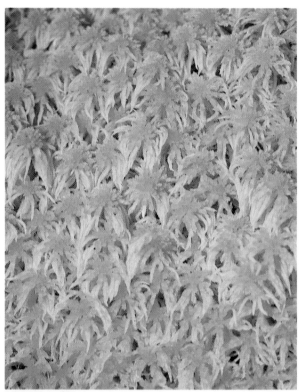

Sphagnum sp. GBB

Baeckea frutescens **Cucur atap**/*Mitthyridium* sp. A pouched hood moss

Above and below: *Leptospermum flavescens* Ti-tree **Cina maki/Gelam bukit** GT

Coelogyne longibracteata GBB

In the sheltered and constantly moist habitat within the mossy forest on mountain ridges, epiphytic plants thrive. Since trees here tend to branch down low, a great many epiphytes grow at eye-level. Orchids—such as *Coelogyne* (above)—are abundant among these. But catching them in bloom is not easy, since many wild orchids display flowers for only a week or two and then may not flower again for a year or more.

The hardiest orchids can survive in very demanding conditions. The scarlet-flowered *Bulbophyllum* (below left) prospers on the exposed and wind-bent branches of a *Leptospermum* tree, while *Epigeneium longipes* can be found clinging to bare rock on a mountain summit. Through their advanced water-retentive adaptations both species are able to grow in direct sunlight, although as epiphytes they have only very limited root systems.

Bulbophyllum skeateanum GT

Epigeneium longipes GT

At almost any time of the year on any mountain in South-East Asia it should be possible to find a rhododendron in bloom, displaying distinctive clusters of trumpet-shaped flowers. Rhododendrons occur wild from North America and Europe through to northern Australia, but the greatest diversity of species is in South-East Asia. Here some are strictly independent plants and some always epiphytic; but several species may adopt either growth habit. A few rhododendrons are found in the lowlands, but most occur only in the mountain forest.

Rhododendron jasminiflorum GBB

Rhododendron durionifolium GM

Rhododendron robinsoni GUK

Rhododendron rugosum GK

Rhododendron longiflorum GJ

Rhododendron malayanum GT

Rhododendron retusum GSN

Nepenthes gracillima GBB

The pitcher plants (*Nepenthes,* **periok kera**) occur on almost all South-East Asian mountains. They are climbing and scrambling plants mostly confined to the tropics. The pitchers themselves are not flowers or fruits, but are modified leaves. The lower part of the stalk is broadened into a leaf-like blade, the true blade forming the pitcher and its lid. This is shaped to attract and trap animal life which is then digested in the liquid contents of the pitcher. Thus the plant gains nutrients otherwise lacking in the poor soils where it tends to grow. Insects are the most common prey, but in species with large pitchers the remains have been found of frogs, birds, and even rats! Nevertheless, for thirsty climbers the liquid in pitchers is generally quite safe to drink.

Identification of *Nepenthes* species is made more difficult because pitchers suspended from aerial parts of the plant are shaped differently from those on the ground. There is also a tendency for species to cross-breed, producing hybrids.

All of the pitcher plants pictured were photographed on mountains, but some species, such as *N. ampullaria* and *N. albo-marginata,* occur in similarly impoverished habitats down to sea level.

Nepenthes macfarlanei GT

Nepenthes albo-marginata GJ

Nepenthes lowii GM

Nepenthes tentaculata GM

Nepenthes villosa GK

Nepenthes ampullaria PT

198

Entoloma sp. (Tricholomataceae) GBB

In the lowland rain forest splashes of colour come much more often from fungi than from flowers. In contrast, blue toadstools (left) and any other fungal forms are a rare sight in the cool conditions of the mountain forest; colourful flowers are, however, relatively common—though it takes an observant eye to find them.

Three pointed pinkish petals is sufficient to identify the tiny *Sonerila* herbs of the forest floor. Of the other three montane flowering plants pictured, *Medinilla* is an epiphyte related to *Sonerila, Aeschynanthus* another epiphyte, and *Scindapsus* a creeper on rocks and tree trunks. These three, as evidenced by their markedly different floral structures, are quite unrelated.

Medinilla scortechinii GBB

Sonerila sp. GM

Sonerila linearis GJ

Aeschynanthus longicalyx var. superba GUK

Scindapsis scortechinii GBB

The summit zone of Gunung Kinabalu (4,101 metres) in Sabah is surely closer in appearance to the surface of the moon than to the surrounding forest-clad foothills. Yet plant life, and some animal life too, does survive even up here at the highest extremity of the tropical rain "forest" in South-East Asia. *Schima*, a relative of the commercial tea plant, grows up to about 3,800 metres; *Rhododendron ericoides* to around 4,000 metres; and the delicate *Potentilla* can be found a stone's throw from the summit. These plants must endure the rush of heavy rains off the rock faces, as well as dehydration during periods of hot sun and dry winds. At night, temperatures on Kinabalu sometimes drop to freezing point.

The vegetation of the mountain holds particular fascination for botanists and plant geographers, with many species endemic to Kinabalu, and many closely related to Australasian, Himalayan, and even European flora.

Alexandra's Peak (4,003 metres) from Gunung Kinabalu summit

GK

Schima brevifolia GK

odododendron ericoides GK

Potentilla borneensis GK

Twin craters, Gunung Sinabung

GSN

Many of the high peaks along the length of Sumatra are volcanoes. Some—including Gunung Sibayak and Gunung Sinabung—are still active, with jets of steam roaring from apertures in the rock within and around the craters. Where the steam condenses, pure crystals of sulphur build up thick encrustations.

Among the loosely packed volcanic rubble of the crater region, and wherever the atmosphere is heavy with sulphurous fumes, no plants grow. But elsewhere there is typical montane vegetation. On Sibayak (2,093 metres) rhododendrons are plentiful, as is the white-flowered *Dianela* of the lily family. On Sinabung (2,451 metres) *Melastoma* is especially abundant, and creeping across bare rock at the upper limit of the vegetation is the tiny *Gaultheria nummularioides*, a relative of the rhododendrons.

Rhododendron rarilepidotum GSB

Dianela javanica GSB

Melastoma ?trachyphyllum GSN

Gaultheria nummularioides GSN

Skeat's Ridge

On Skeat's Ridge

Gunung Tahan, plateau and summit

The highest mountain in Peninsular Malaysia is Gunung Tahan (2,186 metres). The journey there by the standard route takes five days on foot, and a great deal of sweat and effort. Three days are spent in virgin lowland rain forest before the ascent begins, following a long narrow ridge-crest (above left), precipitously steep in places. It is not until the middle of the fifth day that the summit itself is sighted. Gunung Tahan stands on the northern rim of a 20-square-kilometre, basin-shaped plateau (above). The plateau region ranges from about 1,500 to 1,800 metres in altitude, its windswept expanse providing a sudden and dramatic contrast from the densely forested Skeat's ridge leading up to its southern edge.

On flat areas of the plateau the bedrock is exposed in many places; elsewhere it is overlain with a thin peaty soil, swampy and highly acidic. There is little shade. In these demanding conditions grow the terrestrial orchid *Arundina,* and the orchid relative *Burmannia,* as well as the alga *Trentepohlia* (p. 52) and the club-moss *Lycopodium* (p. 61).

On the better-drained rocky slopes leading up to the plateau rim *Nepenthes sanguinea* can be found; here, too, is the tiny mauve *Gentiana,* a rare species closely related to the gentians of the European Alps and the Himalayas.

Gentiana malayana GT

Nepenthes sanguinea GT

na graminifolia GT

Burmannia disticha GT

206

Mossy forest, lush and almost impenetrable, grows in the deeper peaty soil of the gullies that traverse the plateau, and extends up into the saddles above. Many plants that are unable to endure the exposure of the open plateau find a favourable habitat in the shelter of this forest. Epiphytic orchids are abundant, growing at ground level, on tree trunks, and in clumps along branches.

Coelogyne sp. GT

Pholidota globosa GT

Dendrochilum sp. GT

Coelogyne massangeana GT

Psammodynastes pulverulentus Mock viper GS

Animal life on Gunung Tahan includes more than 50 kinds of birds, but very few mammals. Despite the cold, snakes do survive on the mountain; the mock viper, an aggressive but non-venomous species, is one of them. Cicadas can be heard on the plateau, but insects are generally unobtrusive. Such populations that exist are kept in check by the birds, the pitcher plants, and the occasional web-spinning spider.

Cyrtophora sp. GT

PEOPLE OF THE

Bateq family, Sungai Tahan, Pahang, Peninsular Malaysia

RAIN FOREST

A hundred years ago, the Bateq were hardly known even to the Malays who lived along the rivers and were their settled neighbours. They were shy, gentle, peaceful people whose lives were interwoven with the life of the forest. They planted no crops and they rarely stayed longer than a month in any one place. The fulfilment of day-to-day needs was their principal concern and there was little that the rain forest could not provide them.

Today, for most of the Bateq little has changed. A few now have permanent homes and land to cultivate, but the rest still build their thatched lean-to shelters beneath the canopy of tall trees and remain nomadic. At the most perhaps 20 families might stay together, but more often there will be no more than five or six shelters, built a few metres apart, and housing a family each. Still they hunt small game with simple efficient weapons. Still they gather fruits and other edible stems and tubers, as well as forest products for medicinal use. In the benign tropical climate they need little clothing.

Religion for the Bateq is not a separate and distinct part of their culture, but an all-encompassing framework of ideas and actions within which their lives can be conducted in surety and understanding. There is little ritual, and to all outward signs practicality rules their existence to a far greater degree than do supernatural forces. Their culture further encompasses music, song, dance, and various useful crafts. Individuals have few material possessions. The Bateq nowadays are able to speak fluent Malay, but continue primarily to use their own language which has its origins in the Mon-Khmer dialects of Indo-China. While their life is not without risks and dangers, in any misfortune there is acceptance of whatever befalls. Nature gives and nature takes away.

The Bateq number fewer than 2,000 people, living in the lowland forests of northern Pahang and Kelantan in Peninsular Malaysia. The Penan of northern Sarawak and the Kubu of Sumatra are similarly small groups; they, too, follow a nomadic way of life as rain-forest hunters and gatherers.

*   *   *   *   *   *   *   *

It is easy to glamorise the purity and innocence of the existence of primitive-living people, and to envy their remarkable knowledge of the forest environment. But where is any urban-dweller who, seeing this, would relinquish the comforts of modern civilisation? Nevertheless the contrast is disturbing. Everywhere else during this past century human populations have exploded and non-renewable natural resources have been plundered even faster than modern society has grown to depend upon them. Populations of aboriginal groups in their natural environment have apparently hardly changed at all over this period; nor indeed has the forest that supports them. Child mortality is high and life expectancy low; but as long as there is forest to live in, the long-term security of the community is assured.

Communities outside, alas, cannot feel so assured. While it is accepted that the benefits of modern civilisation should not be denied to primitive-living people who freely choose to seek them, it is feared that in the decades to come and following its present course, modern civilisation may well be reduced to battered remnants through self-induced environmental catastrophe, and so forced back into a primeval existence.

Civilisation would appear to be outwitting itself; to be tearing apart from its roots. But a few days spent in the rain forest with the Bateq (or the Penan or the Kubu) helps to shed a different light on the subject. From the roots a clear definition emerges: civilisation is a life in harmony with nature, promising a secure and self-respecting sustainable future for the whole community.

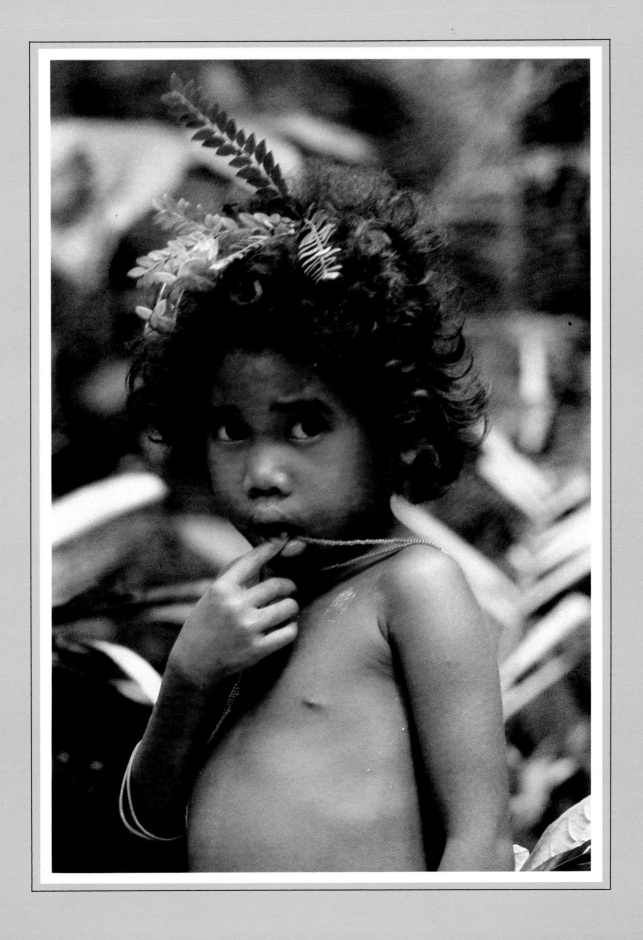

In the hunting-and-gathering economy of the Bateq people of Peninsular Malaysia, most of the gathering work is undertaken by the women. A skilled but time-consuming task is the location of the slender climbing stems of the *Dioscorea* vine, most difficult when the stems have withered and died back during the dormant season, and then the hard labour of digging (above) more than a metre down for the tuberous root or yam. This is the food store of the plant and the carbohydrate staple of the Bateq diet. About ten different kinds of edible yams are known to the Bateq. It is generally the women, too, who construct the ground-level, palm-thatch shelters (pp. 208-9) in establishing a new encampment; and from stems of climbing palms (rattans) they split the outer part of the cane to plait strong strings (opposite) for baskets and for decorative use.

Trionyx cartilagineus Soft-shelled or snapping turtle **Labi-labi** PT

It is the men who do almost all the hunting. On a rod made from the rib of a palm frond, a hook and nylon line may be employed for catching small fish (opposite). A steel-tipped spear is used to kill large fish, but the snapping turtle can be caught by hand should the hunter detect its retreat into an accessible hiding place below the surface of a clear forest stream. Steel implements, notably the parang (jungle knife), are obtained through the Malays of riverside villages, and have been employed by the Bateq for many generations. The bow and arrow was used in former times, but over the past hundred years the blowpipe (right, and overleaf) has taken over as the means for hunting small game such as gibbons, monkeys, squirrels, and hornbills. The Bateq do not hunt or trap large game.

The blowpipe is a precision tool made entirely from materials readily available in the rain forest. A particular kind of bamboo with very long sections between the nodes is selected for the two parts (occasionally only one) which form the barrel. They are joined together (far left) by a section cut from the bark of a tall forest palm, *Arenga* (as on p. 163), and heat-bonded around the junction. This barrel is fitted tightly into an outer bamboo cylinder made up of three separable parts. Woven rattan and carving serve as decoration.

The mouth-piece (left) is made from **damar**, a resin obtained from dipterocarp trees. The quiver and inserts (opposite) are of two more species of bamboo. The darts are made from the split leaf-stalks of the *Arenga* palm; the cone is of lightweight pith; and the tip is coated with a lethal preparation made from the sap of the **ipoh** tree (*Antiaris toxicaria*), and carried in a carefully stoppered bamboo tube. For windage, a soft fluffy "wool" is made from a kind of bark, or from certain leaves or mosses. Assuming the necessary materials from about a dozen different plants are all at hand, a blowpipe and all associated items can be manufactured by one man in a single day.

In experienced hands the blowpipe is deadly accurate on small game within 20 metres.

218

The heritage of the Bateq goes back hundreds of generations. Children are born in the rain forest, and nurtured by it. Through life the Bateq take little from nature that nature alone cannot replace, and leave no wound on the environment that nature alone cannot heal.

Upon death, the body is laid to rest on a bark mat in a specially constructed tree house. All debt to the rain forest is repaid.

APPENDICES

The Identifications

For those who previously have had no special interest in biology, the scientific names of plants and animals may initially appear rather bewildering. These names are given according to a strict hierarchical system which seeks to establish the formal relationships between all living things. Scientific names are recognised world-wide, whereas a common name may vary confusingly from one locality to another.

The ginger flowers on pages 78–81 are all of the same plant family, Zingiberaceae; but within that family there are many genera (singular: genus) such as *Achasma*, *Alpinia*, *Zingiber* .... Each genus may be represented by many species: *Achasma macrocheilos*, *Achasma megalocheilos*, *Achasma triorgyales* .... From external floral characters alone it is easy to distinguish a member of the genus *Achasma* from one of another genus in the family, just as, with experience, members of the Zingiberaceae can be distinguished from plants of other families. Knowledge of scientific names is a stimulus to closer observation of the similarities and differences in nature.

Great care has been taken to ensure that the names ascribed to species pictured in this book are correct. The author accepts full responsibility for any errors that have been made.

Identifications may appear as follows:

(i) *Butorides striatus* Little green heron **Pucung keladi**
—signifying genus and species, English common name, and Malay common name.

(ii) *Globba ?patens*
—signifying that *Globba* is the genus and it is highly likely that the species is *patens*, although this could not be determined with absolute certainty from the material provided.

(iii) *Scutigera sp.*
—signifying that only the genus could be ascertained.

(iv) *Pentaphragma horsfieldii* (formerly named *P. scortechinii*)
—signifying the currently accepted genus and species as well as a formerly accepted name that appears in some older literature still widely used for reference purposes.

(v) N.I.
—signifying that no identification to genus level could be made.

In addition to the identification of the subject there may appear key letters to indicate the locality where the subject was photographed. Where there are no key letters it can be assumed that the locality was in the lowland area of the National Park, Taman Negara (Pahang). Abbreviations for other locations are as follows, with Malaysian states identified in brackets:

BBL — Bukit Batu Luas, Taman Negara (Pahang)
BL — Bukit Lawang, Gunung Leuser National Park, Sumatra
FH — Fraser's Hill (Selangor/Pahang)
GBB — Gunung Bunga Buah (Selangor)
GC — Gua Cemara, Taman Negara (Pahang)
GCM — Gua Cinta Manis (Pahang)
GJ — Gunung Jerai (Kedah)
GK — Gunung Kinabalu, Kinabalu National Park (Sabah)

GM — Gunung Mulu, Gunung Mulu National Park (Sarawak)
GS — Genting Sempah (Selangor/Pahang)
GSB — Gunung Sibayak, Sumatra
GSN — Gunung Sinabung, Sumatra
GT — Gunung Tahan, Taman Negara (Pahang)
GTL — Gua Telinga, Taman Negara (Pahang)
GUK — Gunung Ulu Kali (Selangor/Pahang)
KGR — Klang Gates Ridge (Selangor)
PL — Pulau Langkawi (Kedah)
PT — Pulau Tioman (Pahang)
STS — Sungai Tua (Selangor)
STP — Sungai Tembeling (Pahang)
TLB — Thaleban National Park, Thailand
C — indicates a plant in cultivation or an animal in captivity

In a region where there are so many languages and dialects spoken, it is Malay which is most widely understood. Thus Malay place names (**gunung** for mountain, **sungai** for river, **gua** for cave, **pulau** for island ...) have generally been used unless English names still apply. Of the many local common names which may exist for a widespread species it is the Malay name most universally accepted in Peninsular Malaysia and Singapore that is cited in the identifications and, on occasions, in the text.

The Photography

All of the photographs were taken with Olympus equipment, comprising two camera bodies (OM−1 and OM−2) and five lenses of focal lengths 16 mm. (fish-eye), 28 mm., 50 mm., 100 mm., and 200mm.. In a large proportion of the photographs electronic flash was used, either as sole effective light source (usually two flashes with one off-camera on an extension lead), or to augment natural lighting (usually one flash, off-camera). For the many flash-augmented shots, and for almost all those taken under natural light, a tripod was employed, and exposure times of half a second or longer were frequently used to achieve generous depth of field in low light conditions.

Extension rings were utilised for close-up work, with up to 1:1 magnification achieved using two 14 mm. rings with the 28 mm. lens. For some scenic shots a polarising filter was used to reduce reflections and so intensify colours.

Of several films employed over the years, Kodachrome 64 was that judged best overall for colour rendition on rain-forest subjects and for its fine-grain sharpness; about 80 percent of the photographs in the book were taken using this film.

Rain~Forest National Parks

Although rain forest cloaks many a horizon in South-East Asia, special facilities for public recreation and exploration in the forest are few and far between. The four National Parks described below contain extensive tracts of undisturbed tropical rain forest and offer accommodation, trails, and in some cases informative literature for Park visitors.

TAMAN NEGARA (Peninsular Malaysia)

This National Park covers about 4,300 square kilometres, encompassing lowland, hill, and montane forest, as well as limestone outcrops and navigable rivers. Access to the Park Headquarters at Kuala Tahan is by river only. From Kuala Tahan the visitor is offered river trips (powered or paddled), an extensive network of lowland forest trails, wildlife-rich limestone caves, and observation hides providing good chances to see deer, tapir, and civet cats. Bird-watching opportunities are excellent. The trail to Gunung Tahan begins at Kuala Tahan, and guides are available for the seven to nine-day journey. Comfortable accommodation is provided at Park Headquarters and restaurants serve both local and western food. Further upstream there are lodges with all facilities for self-catering groups. Camping is permitted within the Park. An introductory brochure and a comprehensive booklet on the Park are obtainable from:

> Jabatan Perlindungan Hidupan Liar dan Taman Negara,
> Kilometre 10,
> Jalan Cheras,
> 56100 Kuala Lumpur,
> PENINSULAR MALAYSIA.

All visitor bookings must be made well in advance either in person at the above address or by mail. Taman Negara is closed from mid-November to mid-January during the monsoon season, but can be visited at any other time of year.

THALEBAN NATIONAL PARK (Southern Thailand)

This covers 101 square kilometres adjacent to the Thai-Malaysian border. Much of the Park area is very steep, with extensive areas of virgin forest on both limestone and granite hills. There is a wide variety of wildlife. Thaleban Headquarters is two kilometres north of the border on the little-used road between Kaki Bukit in Perlis (Malaysia) and Hat Yai in Thailand. The road offers good opportunities for observation of primates and birds, and provides easy access to caves and waterfalls. Until marked forest trails are established, visitors to Thaleban who wish to explore beyond the forest fringe must find their own path. For accommodation there are chalets and a hostel, built near the edge of the small natural lake which is the central feature of the Park. Visitors should bring their own food and the means to cook it. Booking in advance is not usually necessary, but the Park may be busy at weekends. Thaleban is open all year round. The wet season is from May to October.

KINABALU NATIONAL PARK (Sabah, Malaysia)

This Park of some 200 square kilometres includes Gunung Kinabalu and much of its forested foothills. At Park Headquarters just off the Kota Kinabalu-Ranau road the altitude is around 1,500 metres. Here there are many well graded trails leading through hill forest, with clear streams and look-out points along the way. More than 400 trees have been numbered and identified. The main attraction, however, is the mountain itself which can be climbed with a guide in a two-day return trip; but it is well worth spending more than one night in the accommodation huts on the high slopes. Both the hill forest and the mountain flanks are rich in bird life, and the vegetation is of special interest even to non-botanists. At Headquarters, comfortable accommodation is available in self-catering bungalows and a hostel. There is a restaurant and shop. Useful Park literature is obtainable from the information centre.

A second visitor centre is at Poring Hot Springs, reached via Ranau. Here there is a camping area and small bungalows. As well as bathing pools there are walking trails through lowland forest.

All bookings for the Park should be made well in advance through:

Kinabalu Park Warden,
P.O. Box 10626,
88806 Kota Kinabalu,
SABAH,
MALAYSIA.

GUNUNG LEUSER NATIONAL PARK (North Sumatra)

This vast reserve of about 8,000 square kilometres protects a wide range of habitat types from lowland swamp forest to montane scrub. It is a vital sanctuary for the Sumatran rhinoceros and other endangered species. At the Orang Utan Rehabilitation Centre, Bohoruk, young orang utans retrieved from illegal captivity are reintroduced to their natural habitat. Park visitors may stay at the Centre; there is a single bungalow and a camping area nearby. Several clearly marked trails have been established through steep forest ranging in altitude from 200 to 400 metres. Orang utans are quite easily sighted in the forest at any time of day. The Rehabilitation Centre is less than 30 minutes' easy walk from the village of Bukit Lawang. By local buses from Medan via Bohoruk the trip to Bukit Lawang takes three to four hours. A Park entry permit must be obtained beforehand from the address below; maximum duration of stay is three days.

A second visitor area is under development at Lawe Gurah, 245 kilometres from Medan via Kutacane, and about ten hours' journey by bus. Here, at an altitude of 330 metres and above, there are clear streams, a hot spring, and an extensive area of undisturbed forest. There is a research station nearby at Ketambe.

The highest peaks within the Park are Gunung Leuser (3,466 metres) and Gunung Kemiri (3,314 metres). Both are in very remote areas and not accessible to general visitors.

Details and permits can be obtained by calling personally at:

Departmen Kehutanan,
Balai Konservasi Sumber Daya Alam I Medan,
Jalan Sisingamangaraja, Km. 5.5,
Medan, NORTH SUMATRA.

Acknowledgements

To En Mohd. Khan bin Momin Khan, Director-General of the Department of Wildlife and National Parks, Peninsular Malaysia, for the opportunity to live and work in Taman Negara and so lay the foundation for this book; to the Bateq of the Tembeling valley who so willingly shared their profound knowledge of the rain forest on so many journeys and explorations; and to the Malay community of Kuala Tahan for the kindness shown and assistance given over my years resident there, and on numerous subsequent visits.

To the many companions through the years who, in forest or caves or on mountains, and often in uncomfortable circumstances, held torchlight or flash-gun or reflector or breath as well as the occasional bat or snake or snapping turtle, all with admirable patience and forbearance, during the invariably complicated process of my taking a seemingly simple photograph.

To those who agreed to bear the brunt of the arduous and often frustrating task of identifying, usually from photographs alone, a total of more than 300 botanical and zoological subjects—Dr B.C. Stone of Universiti Malaya, Mr D.H. Murphy of the National University of Singapore, Dr Chang Kiaw Lan and En Mohd. Shah bin Mohd. Noor of the Botanic Gardens, Singapore, Mr K.M. Kochummen of the Forest Research Institute, Kepong, and Dr John Dransfield of the Royal Botanic Gardens, Kew. To the many others who assisted with individual identifications: Professor E.J.H. Corner, Mr H.S. Barlow, Mr Vincent Tung; from the British Museum (Natural History), Dr Nick Arnold, Mr P.D. Hillyard, Mr D. Macfarlane, Ms Judith Marshall, Mr F.E. Naggs, Mr Lee Rogers, Mr Bruce Townsend, and Mr F.R. Wanless; from the Royal Botanic Garden, Edinburgh, Mr Bill Burtt, Ms Rosemary Smith, and Dr Roy Watling; from the Forest Research Institute, Kepong, Dr Francis Ng, Dr Tho Yow Pong, and Mr Wong Khoon Meng; from the Royal Botanic Gardens, Kew, Mr H.M. Burkill, Dr Barbara Croxall, Dr David Pegler, and Mr Jeffrey Wood; from London University, Dr Jackie Reilly; from the National University of Singapore, Mr Chou Loke Meng; from Taman Negara, En Jasmi bin Abdul and staff; from Universiti Kebangsaan Malaysia, Dr Farah Ghani; from Universiti Malaya, Dr Haji Mohamed, Dr Kiew Bong Heang, Mr M. Ratnasabapathy, Dr E. Soepadmo, and Dr David Wells; and from Universiti Pertanian Malaysia, Dr Ruth Kiew. To Dr Dick Vane-Wright who co-ordinated identification work at the British Museum, and Dr Salleh Mohd. Noor who kindly granted permission for F.R.I. Kepong staff to assist.

To Mr Louis Ratnam of the Department of Wildlife and National Parks, Mr Leyu Chong Hua of the Malaysian Meteorological Service, and staff of the Geology Faculty, Universiti Malaya, for assistance with technical details.

To Tunku Mohd. Nazim Yaacob and John Dransfield for text criticism on matters zoological and botanical respectively, and to Gilbert Khoo, Avril Fox, Henry Barlow, and Helen Riley for much constructive hole-shooting and subsequent repair and polish to the general content and expression.

To En Abdullah Thamby and Victor Chin for advice on aspects of the book design and layout; and to Mr K.S. Maniam and En Ma'arif bin Mohd. Yusoh for especially conscientious work on the typesetting and proof-reading respectively.

To Mr Lim Kok Peng for advice on selection of photographs and to Mr Winston Ee for his meticulous work on the colour separations; and to the Malayan Nature Society and the Malaysian Zoological Society for permission to publish several photographs copyrighted to them.

To H.S.B., O.C.H., J.S.H.S. and C.R.H. for accommodation, commiseration, counsel and encouragement.

And finally, to my father, for his understanding.

To all these people, my heartfelt thanks.

K.R.

Selected Bibliography

On the rain forest in general, and specific localities:

LEE, D. (1980). *The sinking ark, environmental problems in Malaysia and Southeast Asia.* Kuala Lumpur: Heinemann Asia.

LUPING, M., CHIN, W., AND DINGLEY, E.R. (eds.) (1978). *Kinabalu, summit of Borneo.* Kota Kinabalu: The Sabah Society.

RICHARDS, P.W. (1952). *The tropical rain forest.* Cambridge University Press.

SOEPADMO, E. AND HO, T.H. (eds.) (1971). *A guide to Batu Caves.* Kuala Lumpur: Malayan Nature Society.

WALLACE, A.R. (1980). *The Malay archipelago.* Reprint. New York: Dover Publications.

WHITMORE, T.C. (1984) *Tropical rain forests of the Far East.* 2nd ed. London: Oxford University Press.

For introductory reading on plant life and animal life:

HOLTTUM, R.E. (1954). *Plant life in Malaya.* Kuala Lumpur: Longman Malaysia.

TWEEDIE, M.W.F. AND HARRISON, J.L. (1970). *Malayan animal life.* 3rd ed. Kuala Lumpur: Longman Malaysia.

YONG, H.S. (1981). *Magnificent plants.* Kuala Lumpur: Tropical Press.

For identification of plants:

CORNER, E.J.H. (1952). *Wayside trees of Malaya.* 2nd ed. Singapore: Government Printing Office.

GILLILAND, H.B. (1971). *A revised flora of Malaya,* vol. 3: *Grasses of Malaya.* Singapore: Government Printing Office.

HENDERSON, M.R. (1954). *Malayan wild flowers.* 2 vols. Kuala Lumpur: Malayan Nature Society.

HOLTTUM, R.E. (1953). *A revised flora of Malaya,* vol. I: *Orchids of Malaya.* Singapore: Government Printing Office.

HOLTTUM, R.E. (1966). *A revised flora of Malaya,* vol. 2: *Ferns of Malaya.* Singapore: Government Printing Office.

JOHNSON, A. (1977). *The ferns of Singapore island.* 2nd ed. Singapore University Press.

JOHNSON, A. (1980). *Mosses of Singapore and Malaysia.* Singapore University Press.

SMYTHIES, B.E. (1965). *Common Sarawak trees.* Kuching: Borneo Literature Bureau.

SYMINGTON, C.F. (1943). *Foresters' manual of dipterocarps* (Malayan Forest Records No. 16). Kuala Lumpur: Forest Department.

VAN STEENIS, C.G.G.J. (1962). *The mountain flora of Java.* Leiden: E.J. Brill.

WHITMORE, T.C. (1977). *Palms of Malaya.* 2nd ed. Kuala Lumpur: Oxford University Press.

WHITMORE, T.C. AND NG, F.S.P. (eds.) (1972, 1973, 1978). *Tree flora of Malaya.* 3 vols. Kuala Lumpur: Longman Malaysia.

For identification of animals:

BARLOW, H.S. (1982). *An introduction to the moths of South East Asia.* Kuala Lumpur: Malayan Nature Society.

CORBETT, A.S. AND PENDLEBURY, H.M. (1978). *The butterflies of the Malay Peninsula.* 3rd ed. revised by J.N. Eliot. Kuala Lumpur: Malayan Nature Society.

KING, B., WOODCOCK, M., AND DICKINSON, E.C. (1975). *A field guide to the birds of South-East Asia.* London: Collins.

LIM, B.L. (1982). *Poisonous snakes of Peninsular Malaysia.* 2nd ed. Kuala Lumpur: Malayan Nature Society.

MADOC, G.C. (1956). *An introduction to Malayan birds.* Kuala Lumpur: Malayan Nature Society.

MEDWAY, LORD (1977). *Mammals of Borneo.* 2nd ed. (Monograph No. 7). Kuala Lumpur: Malaysian Branch of the Royal Asiatic Society.

MEDWAY, LORD (1978). *The wild mammals of Malaya.* 2nd ed. Kuala Lumpur: Oxford University Press.

SMYTHIES, B.E. (1981). *The birds of Borneo.* 3rd ed. revised by the Earl of Cranbrook. Kuala Lumpur: The Sabah Society and the Malayan Nature Society.

TUNG, V.W.Y. (1983). *Common Malaysian beetles.* Kuala Lumpur: Longman Malaysia.

TWEEDIE, M.W.F. (1983). *The snakes of Malaya.* 3rd ed. Singapore: National Printers (Pte.) Ltd.

YONG, H.S. (1983). *Malaysian butterflies—an introduction.* Kuala Lumpur: Tropical Press.

INDEX

Malay Names

THAILAND

Hat Yai

21
17
7

PENANG

PENINSULAR
MALAYSIA

13
14
1
5
20

Banda Aceh

Medan

STRAIT OF MALACCA

6
3
15
4
19

2
12
11

Kuantan

10
16
18

Kuala Lumpur

SIMEULUE

ANA
ISL

M A

SINGAPORE

NIAS

RIAU

LINGGA

Pakanbaru

SUMATRA

Padang

MENTAWAI
ISLANDS

Telanaipura

BANG

INDIAN
OCEAN

Palembang

Bengkulu

Tekutbetung

Jaka

FORESTED AREAS IN SOUTH-EAST ASIA

KEY

VEGETATION

☐ forests of peat swamps, fresh-water swamps, and mangroves

☐ lowland tropical rain forest, evergreen and semi-evergreen; also encompassing areas of limestone vegetation and heathlands

☐ montane tropical rain forest

☐ deforested areas: settlements, croplands, plantations, tin mines etc.

N.B. Areas designated as forested include both primary and secondary (logged) forest.

Principal source: Whitmore, T.C. (1984) *A vegetation map of Malesia at scale 1:5 million. Journal of Biogeography* 11:461-471

PHOTOGRAPHY SITES

1 Bukit Batu Luas (BBL)
2 Bukit Lawang, Gunung Leuser National Park (BL)
3 Fraser's Hill (FH)
4 Gunung Bunga Buah (GBB)
5 Gua Cemara, Taman Negara (GC)
6 Gua Cinta Manis (GCM)
7 Gunung Jerai (GJ)
8 Gunung Kinabalu, Kinabalu National Park (GK)
9 Gunung Mulu, Gunung Mulu National Park (GM)

10 Genting Sempah (GS)
11 Gunung Sibayak (GSB)
12 Gunung Sinabung (GSN)
13 Gunung Tahan, Taman Negara (GT)
14 Gua Telinga, Taman Negara (GTL)
15 Gunung Ulu Kali (GUK)
16 Klang Gates Ridge (KGR)
17 Pulau Langkawi (PL)
18 Pulau Tioman (PT)
19 Sungai Tua (STS)
20 Sungai Tembeling (STP)
21 Thaleban National Park (TLB)